Early years activities

MATHS

PHOTOCOPIABLES

49
⑮ £1·75.

impact

MATHS HOMEWORK

Published by Scholastic Publications Ltd,
Villiers House,
Clarendon Avenue,
Leamington Spa,
Warwickshire CV32 5PR

© **1994 Scholastic Publications Ltd**
Text © 1994 University of North
London Enterprises Ltd

UNIVERSITY OF
NORTH LONDON

Activities by the IMPACT Project
at the University of North London,
collated and rewritten by Ruth
Merttens and Ros Leather

Editors Jane Wright and Jo Saxelby-Jennings
Assistant editors Sophie Jowett and Joanne Boden
Designer Tracey Ramsey
Series designer Anna Oliwa
Illustrations John Davey
Cover illustration Roger Wade Walker

Designed using Aldus Pagemaker
Processed by Pages Bureau, Leamington Spa
Artwork by Pages Bureau, Leamington Spa
Printed in Great Britain
by Clays Ltd, St Ives plc

British Library Cataloguing-in-Publication Data
A catalogue record for this book is
available from the British Library.

ISBN 0-590-53162-X

impact
C O N T E N T S

Early years activities

impact

CONTENTS

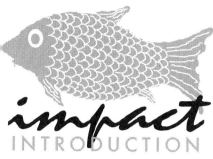

impact
INTRODUCTION

This series of IMPACT books is designed to help you run a non-traditional homework scheme. Through the use of take-home maths activities, children can share maths with a parent/carer in the context of the home. The results of these activities then feed back into the classwork at school.

IMPACT works through the following processes:
● Teachers plan their maths for the next few weeks as usual and consider which parts might usefully be done at home.
● Teachers look through selected activities which fit in with what they are planning.
● The activities are photocopied and sent home with the children every week or fortnight.
● The results of each activity are brought back into the classroom by the children and form part of the following week's classwork.

In practice this process will be slightly different in each classroom and in each school. Teachers may adapt it to fit their own way of working and the ethos of the school in which they work. Most schools send out IMPACT activities fortnightly, although some do send it weekly. There is some evidence to suggest that weekly activities get a slightly better response and help to raise standards more effectively than fortnightly, but this is not conclusive. The important point is that

each teacher should feel comfortable with how often the IMPACT activities are used in his/her class.

Planning

When you, the teacher, are looking at your work and deciding what maths, roughly speaking, you plan to be doing over the next few weeks, all that is necessary is to consider which parts may usefully be done or practised at home. It is helpful if, over a period of time, a range of activities are chosen in order to vary the mathematical experience in the home and the type and amount of follow-up required in class.

The activities tend to fall into three broad categories:
● Activities which practise a skill – these are useful in that they can be followed up in the routine classwork. They must be carefully selected by the teacher according to the level of the children.
● Activities which collect data – these lead into work on data-handling and representation.
● Activities in which children measure or make something – this produces an object or some measurements to be used later in class.

The activities in this book are divided into three sections according to age: Three year olds, Four year olds and Five year olds. There are two pages of teachers' notes relating to the individual activities at the beginning of each section.

Working with parents

It is important for the success of IMPACT that the activities taken home are seen by the parents to be 'proper' maths. We always suggest, at least until IMPACT is up and running and parents' confidence in it is well established, that activities are chosen which have a clearly mathematical purpose. Save the more

'wacky' activities until later! You will get a much better response if parents believe that what they are doing is maths.

Each activity contains a note to parents which explains the purpose of the activity and how they can best help. The activities should be accompanied by an IMPACT diary, enabling parents and children to make their comments. The diaries provide a mechanism by means of which an efficient parent-teacher dialogue is established. Through these diaries, which last up to two years depending upon the frequency of the IMPACT tasks, teachers obtain valuable feedback both about children's performances on specific maths tasks and about the tasks themselves. Parents are able to alert the teacher to weaknesses and strengths and nothing about the child's performance in maths comes as a big surprise at the end of the year or when the statutory assessments are administered. The diaries are a crucial part of this homework scheme and are available from IMPACT Supplies Ltd.

Making the most of IMPACT

The quickest way to reduce the number of children who share the maths at home is to ignore or be negative about the work they bring back into school. When the children come running into the classroom, tripping over the string which went twice round their cat, it is difficult to welcome them all individually but it is crucial that the activities done at home are followed up in classwork. The nature and type of this follow-up work depends very much upon the nature of the activity, and specific suggestions are made in the teachers' notes. However, some general points apply:
● Number activities, such as games, can often be repeated in a more formalised way in the classwork. For example, if the children have been playing a dice game,

throwing two dice and adding the totals, they can continue to do this in the classroom, but this time they can record all the 'sums' in their maths book. This applies to any skills-practice activity.
● Data-collecting activities, of any description, need to be followed up by allowing the children to work together in small groups to collate, analyse and represent their joint data. This will inevitably involve discussion as to how their data was obtained, and any problems they encountered while obtaining it.
● If the children have made or measured something at home, the information or the object needs to be used as part of the resulting classwork. This will not be too difficult since this type of activity is selected precisely in order to provide the measurements or shapes for use in class.

Many of the activities can lead to an attractive display or enable the teacher to make a class book. Such a book does not have to be 'grand'. It can be simply five or six large sheets of sugar paper folded in the middle and stitched/stapled with the children's work mounted inside it. The children love these books, and they make a fine record of their work. An IMPACT display board in the school entrance hall gives parents a sense that their work at home is appreciated.

Help with implementing IMPACT

Schools that wish to get IMPACT started by means of a series of staff meetings or in-service days may like to purchase the IMPACT INSET pack. This is available from IMPACT Supplies Ltd, PO Box 1, Woodstock, Oxon OX20 1HB.

Useful telephone numbers

IMPACT Central Office (for information and assistance): 071 607 2789 Ext. 6349 at the University of North London.
IMPACT Supplies Ltd (for diaries and INSET pack): 0993 812895.

Teachers' Notes
THREE YEAR OLDS

How many clothes? The children can draw their favourite piece of clothing on to a squared piece of paper. You can make a pictogram of these according to the number of pieces of clothing each child had, for example, they put their picture in the '4' column if they were wearing four pieces of clothing. Who was wearing the most?

Towers toppling over! The children can count how many tins there are in two of their towers. Can they build a tower of bricks that high? Make a graph using the children's numbers by colouring in a tin with each number on it and placing it in the same numbered column.

Three little birds Talk about the concepts of first, second and third. Ask the children to find the third page in a book. How do they do it? Line them up in order of height. Who is the first, second and third? Make three large and beautiful bird pictures to put up on the wall at your playgroup or nursery.

Lots of three The children can compare their sets. Make up as many sets of three as you can. What are the criteria for things being in the same set (for example, three things of the same colour or made from the same material). Make some sets where the children have to guess the common factor.

Magic three Make magic wands in the nursery or playgroup. Can some wands count to more than three? Make up some sets for each wand to practise with.

Search for three Talk about body numbers; that is, the parts the children have two of, the parts they have five of and so on. Can they find something for each number? For example, 1 head 2 eyes, 3 sticky-out pieces on the head (2 ears, 1 nose), 4 fingers on each hand, 5 toes on each foot and so on. Make a body outline with all these numbers on it.

Making a collection The children can make sets like this in playgroup or nursery – only making sure that these are made with large objects! It is important to emphasise that the size of the things in the set does not affect the number. The children can practise counting by pointing to or touching the object as they say the number.

Big foot! In class, find out how many Multilink bricks or small crayons fit along each foot and then along each arm length. Write down each number. Which number is the biggest? Arrange all the 'big feet' in a long line from shortest to longest! Display these on the wall. Do the same with the arm lengths.

Toy weight Discuss how big things can be light, and small things can be heavy. Bring in some examples of your own. For example, a large amount of cotton wool is light, but a small amount of lead is heavy. Display their toy pictures in two sets – light and heavy. Talk about the heaviest toy and the lightest!

Big person! Discuss how many objects each of the children used in their lines.

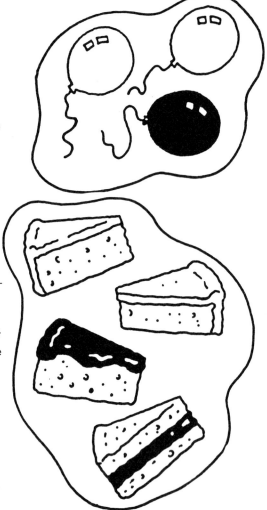

They can then draw a picture of the person they measured on a small oblong piece of paper and stick it on a pictograph above the number of objects they used to measure that person. For example, if seven things were used to make a line as long as dad, then stick the picture of dad above the 7 on the graph. Discuss why the people who had the most things used to measure them may NOT be the tallest (necessarily)!

Birthday cakes Make some cardboard birthday cakes in class and put the right numbers of candles on them. How many cakes are there? How many candles in all? Discuss what might happen if you had a cake the day you were born! What number would be drawn on it? Draw the right numbers on each of the other cakes.

Special day Display all the children's drawings in the appropriate sets, each abelled with a day of the week. Are there any sets which have no drawings in? Which day has most pictures in it? Which is your favourite day? Which is, say, mummy's favourite day? Practise saying the days of the week together 'on the rug'.

The two game The children could be encouraged to set up a '2 table'. Each child could find two objects and place them by a printed number 2. Encourage the children to find a partner. One child could be 'Peter' and the other one 'Paul', and they could sing and act out the song 'Two little dicky-birds'.

The three game The children could make large triangles. These could be used to count sides and angles up to three. They could then be tessellated to make a large display. The children could be encouraged to paint a large number 3 and to cut out and stick three pictures (from a magazine) on to their sheet of paper.

Handprint patterns The children may like to repeat this activity using potatoes or sponge prints. Three or four children could each have a different colour and they could repeat the colour pattern taking different turns, for example, 1 yellow, 2 red, 3 blue, 1 yellow, 2 red, 3 blue and so on.

My favourite teddy costs 4p The children may like to set up a teddy shop and price their teddies. Use real 1p coins for buying the teddies and encourage the children to use the correct number of coins when buying teddies from the shop.

Sweet shopping Give the children time to talk about what they have bought. Have any children bought the same item? The children could group themselves depending on the price or type of item bought.

Sorting bronze coins Play this game with a few children sitting in a circle. You will need some 2p and 1p coins in the centre of the circle. Challenge the children. For example, 'Can we all find 3p? How many ways can we make 3p?' Encourage the children to tap each of the 2p coins twice when counting.

Money snake The children could display their snakes in a garden of flowers. Each flower has a different price: blue flowers with three petals cost 3p, yellow flowers with two petals cost 2p, red flowers with four petals cost 4p and so on. The children could 'buy' and 'sell' the flowers. Encourage them to count aloud as they buy or sell.

My favourite circle Let the children arrange themselves in order of the size of their circles. Who has the largest circle? How do they know that it is the largest circle? How many circles can they find that are smaller, larger or the same size as theirs? How far will the circle travel when it is rolled once? How can they find out?

impact MATHS HOMEWORK

How many clothes?

● How many clothes are you wearing?

● Next time you get dressed or undressed, count all the articles of clothing that you are wearing. How many are there? Do you count each sock as one?

Towers toppling over!

- How many tins can you pile one on top of the other before they all fall down?

- Pile as many as you can.

- When you have built a high tower, can you draw it on the back of this sheet? Be careful to draw in the right number of tins!

_____and

child

_____

helper(s)

_____

did this activity together

_____and

child

_____

helper(s)

_____

did this activity together

Three little birds

● Draw three birds on three different pieces of paper. Draw them as big as you can.

● Ask someone to cut them out. Now stick them up in a line along the wall. Which is first? Which is second? Which is third?

impact MATHS HOMEWORK

Lots of three

● How many sets of three things can you find on this page?

Dear Parent or Carer

We are encouraging children to recognise both the number 3, and how many it represents.
   Talk about the fact that the child is three years old. Which numbers are less than three? Which numbers are more than three?

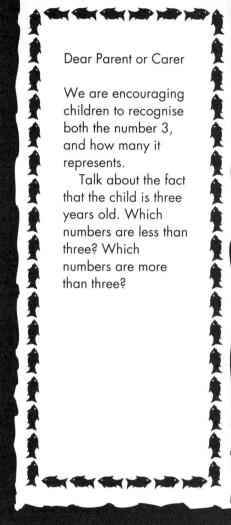

_____and
child

_____
helper(s)

_____

did this activity together

Magic three

Most magicians think that 3 is a magic number!

● Ask someone to make you a magic wand out of a piece of rolled up newspaper, taped and painted black with a white tip.

● Use your wand to count to three!

'One, two, three and....'

What magic can you do?

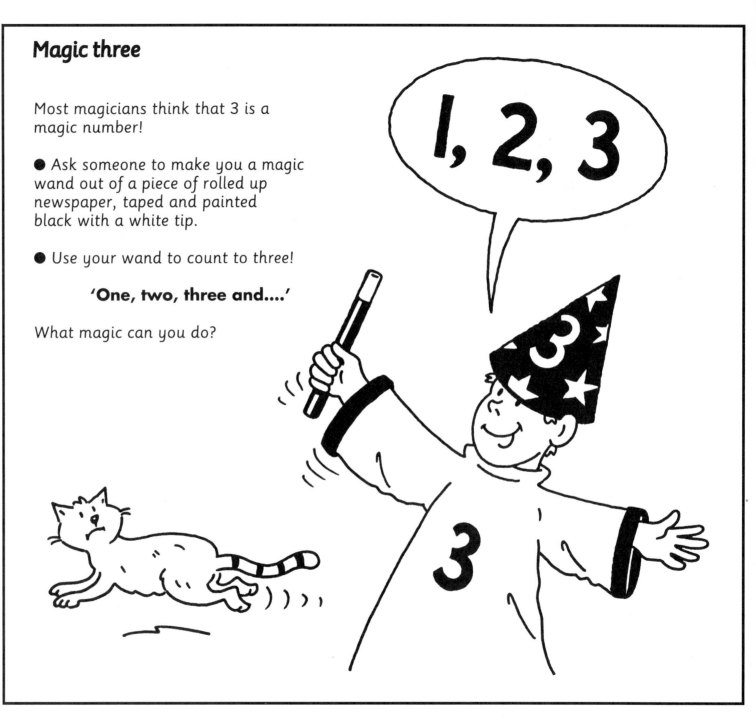

Search for three

We have two hands.   We have two feet. We have ten toes.   We have two eyes.

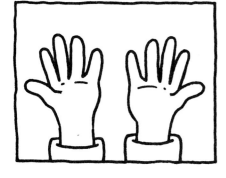 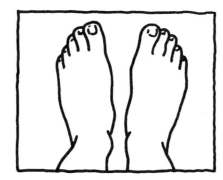 

● What can you find three of? Look for examples of three. Perhaps you have three freckles or three buttons on a jersey?

Dear Parent or Carer

Help your child to recognise sets of three. Talk about the fact that two is one less than three. What number is one more than three?

How old is your child now (3)? How old will they be next year (4)?

_____and

child

_____

helper(s)

_____

did this activity together

Dear Parent or Carer

Help your child to count carefully. It helps if they touch each thing as they count it, saying the number out loud.

_____and

child

_____

helper(s)

_____

did this activity together

Making a collection

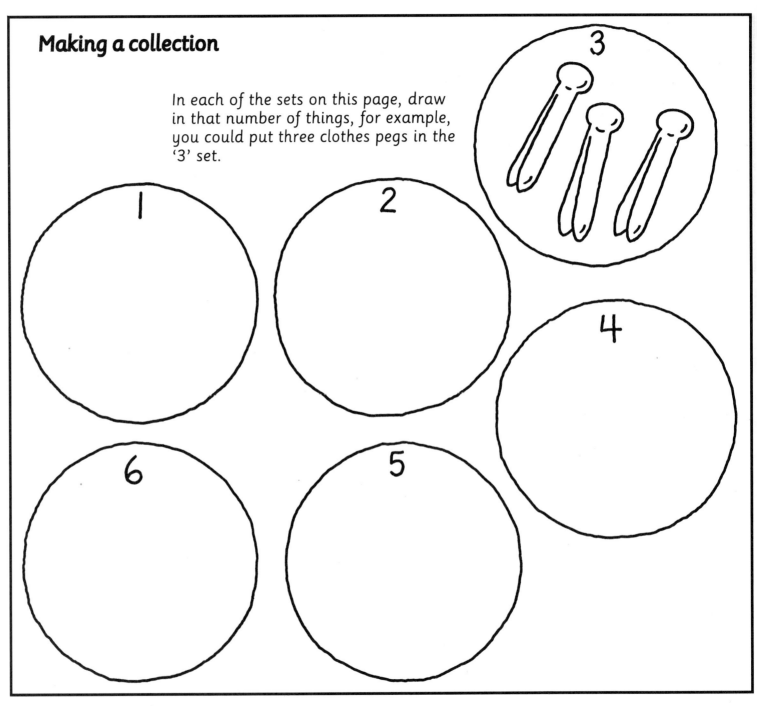

In each of the sets on this page, draw in that number of things, for example, you could put three clothes pegs in the '3' set.

impact MATHS HOMEWORK

Big foot!

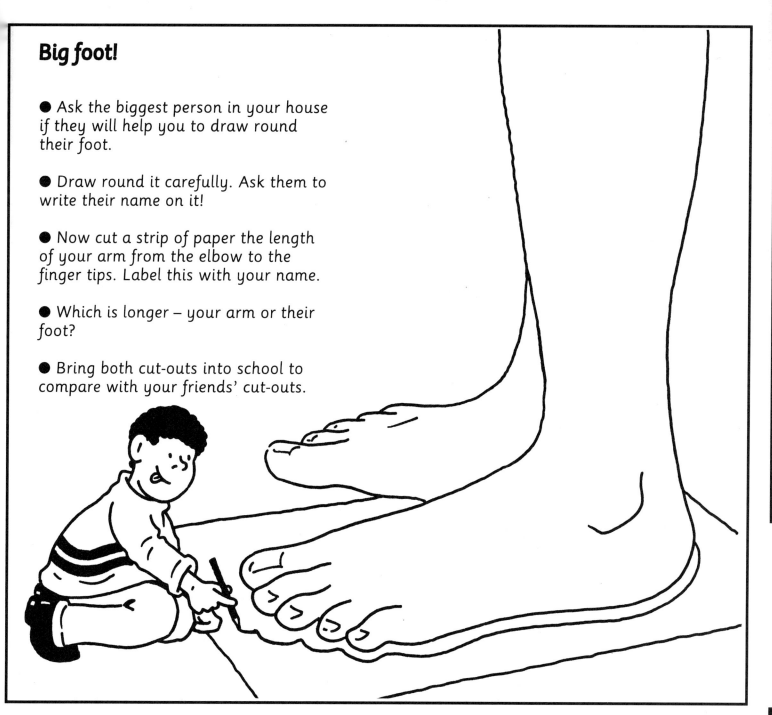

● Ask the biggest person in your house if they will help you to draw round their foot.

● Draw round it carefully. Ask them to write their name on it!

● Now cut a strip of paper the length of your arm from the elbow to the finger tips. Label this with your name.

● Which is longer – your arm or their foot?

● Bring both cut-outs into school to compare with your friends' cut-outs.

Dear Parent or Carer

We are talking about 'longer than' and 'shorter than' here. Discuss these ideas with your child. Look for things which are longer than their arm. And look for things which are shorter (this is sometimes harder!).

_____and

child

_____

helper(s)

_____

did this activity together

impact MATHS HOMEWORK

Dear Parent or Carer

We are discussing heavier and lighter here. It is important that small children come to realise that big things are not necessarily the heaviest, and vice versa. These are difficult ideas which take a lot of getting used to.

_____and

child

_____

helper(s)

_____

did this activity together

Toy weight

- Find a light toy which is big – like a teddy!

- Find a heavy toy which is small – like a toy car.

- Which is your heaviest toy? Is it your biggest toy?

- Which is your lightest toy? Is it your smallest toy?

- Draw your favourite toy below and bring your picture into school.

impact MATHS HOMEWORK

Big person!

● Find the tallest person in your house and ask them if they would mind lying down on the floor.

● Collect enough things to make a line as long as they are. How many things does it take?

● Ask someone to write a list of all the things you had in your line! Bring your list into school.

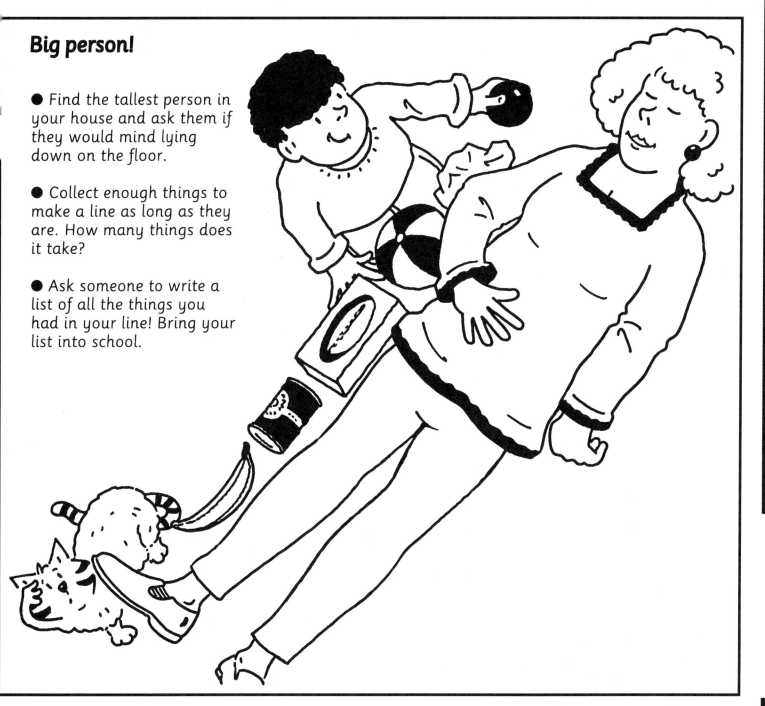

Dear Parent or Carer

We are talking about length and starting some basic work on measurement. Talk to your child about how long their line is. Help them to find some suitable things so that they don't need too many – for example, magazines, belts, socks, teddies, books and so on.

_____and

child

_____

helper(s)

_____

did this activity together

_____and

child

_____

helper(s)

_____

did this activity together

Birthday cakes

Below is a picture of some birthday cakes.

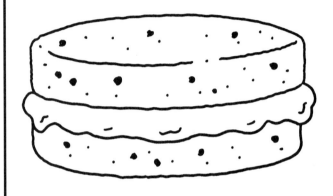
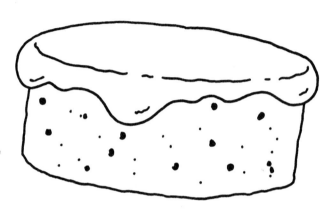
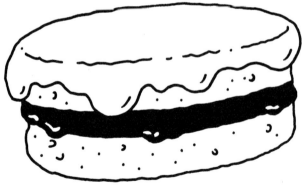

● Imagine that one was the cake you had on your very first birthday.
The second one was the cake you had on your 2nd birthday.
The third one was the cake you had on your 3rd birthday.

● Draw the right number of candles on each cake.

● How many candles are there?

Special day

● Is one day of the week a special day for you?

● Which is your favourite day? Talk about what happens then. What do you do that's special?

● Below, draw a picture of what you do, and ask your helper to write the day beside it. Bring your drawing into school.

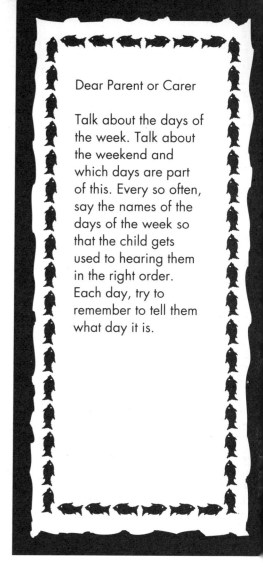

Dear Parent or Carer

Talk about the days of the week. Talk about the weekend and which days are part of this. Every so often, say the names of the days of the week so that the child gets used to hearing them in the right order. Each day, try to remember to tell them what day it is.

_____and

child

_____

helper(s)

_____

did this activity together

_____and

child

_____

helper(s)

_____

did this activity together

The two game

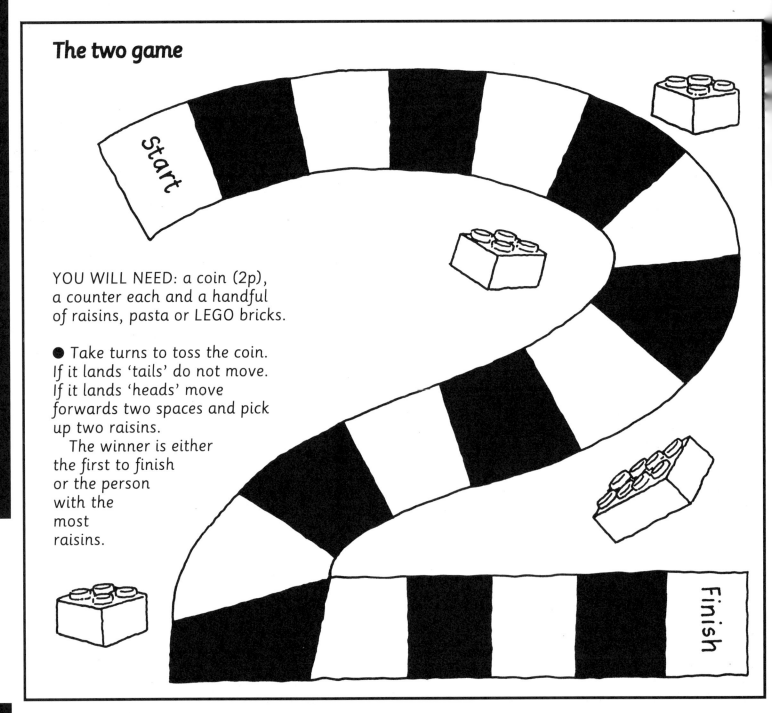

YOU WILL NEED: a coin (2p), a counter each and a handful of raisins, pasta or LEGO bricks.

● Take turns to toss the coin. If it lands 'tails' do not move. If it lands 'heads' move forwards two spaces and pick up two raisins.
    The winner is either the first to finish or the person with the most raisins.

impact MATHS HOMEWORK

The three game

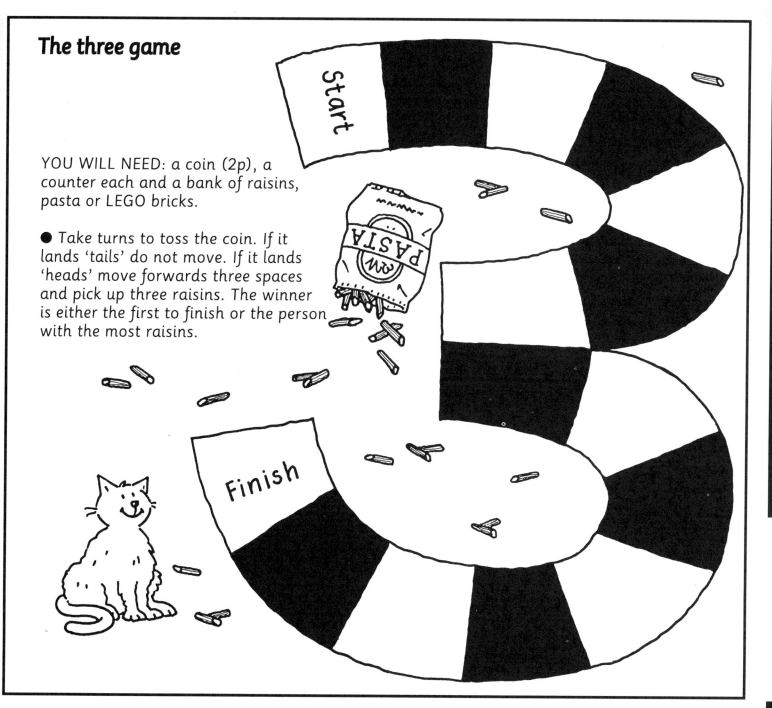

YOU WILL NEED: a coin (2p), a counter each and a bank of raisins, pasta or LEGO bricks.

● Take turns to toss the coin. If it lands 'tails' do not move. If it lands 'heads' move forwards three spaces and pick up three raisins. The winner is either the first to finish or the person with the most raisins.

Start

Finish

PASTA

_____and

child

_____

helper(s)

_____

did this activity together

Dear Parent or Carer

This is great fun but messy! Can your child make a handprint pattern, for example, red hand, blue hand, red hand, blue hand or red, red, blue, blue? Ask your child to talk about the pattern being created.

_____and

child

_____

helper(s)

_____

did this activity together

Handprint patterns

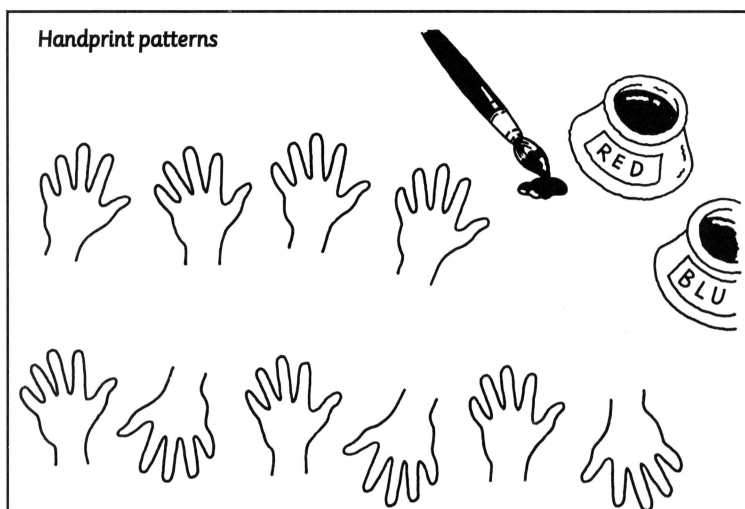

YOU WILL NEED: a bowl of soapy water nearby for washing mucky hands, an old shirt as a cover-up, plenty of paper (newspaper will do) and paint.

● On a large piece of paper, make patterns with your handprint. What colours will you use?

impact MATHS HOMEWORK

My favourite teddy costs 4p

YOU WILL NEED: four 1p coins and a pencil.

● Draw round the dotted line to see teddy.

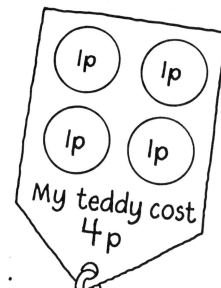

My teddy cost 4p

● Now place each penny on one of the circles above, counting as you go.

Dear Parent or Carer

Encourage your child to sort out the 1p coins from your loose change. Give help in placing four 1p coins on to the circles. Help your child to touch and move each coin as it is counted.

Then your child may like to colour in the teddy.

_____and

child

_____

helper(s)

_____

did this activity together

Dear Parent or Carer

Help your child to buy a small item from a shop (no more than 10p). Give help in choosing and counting the 1p coins needed to buy the item.

_____and

child

_____

helper(s)

_____

did this activity together

Sweet shopping

● How many 1p coins would you need to buy each of the sweets below?

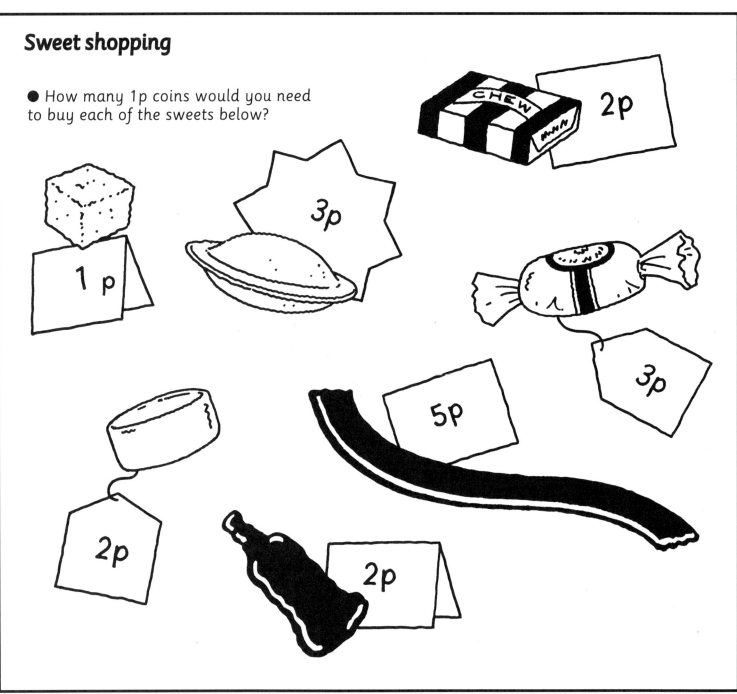

Sorting bronze coins

- What is the difference between the 2p coin and the 1p coin?

2p coins	1p coins

- Sort a pile of bronze coins (coppers) into 2p coins on the 2p drawn above and 1p coins on the 1p drawn above.

Dear Parent or Carer

Help your child to sort out the bronze coins in your pocket or purse into sets. Using the large drawings of the coins, help your child to distinguish between the larger 2p and the smaller 1p coins. You may like to count how many 1p coins you have in the set.

Your child may like to look at the other coins and sort them into two categories, for example: round/ not round; shining/ dull; silver/not silver.

_____and

child

_____

helper(s)

_____

did this activity together

Dear Parent or Carer

Please help your child to find all the 1p coins from your purse or pocket and to fit them along the snake in the circles. It is important that the children touch each coin as it is counted.

Help your child to trace the number 3 with their finger, always beginning at the top.

Your child may like to make larger or shorter snakes and count the coins.

_____and

child

_____

helper(s)

_____

did this activity together

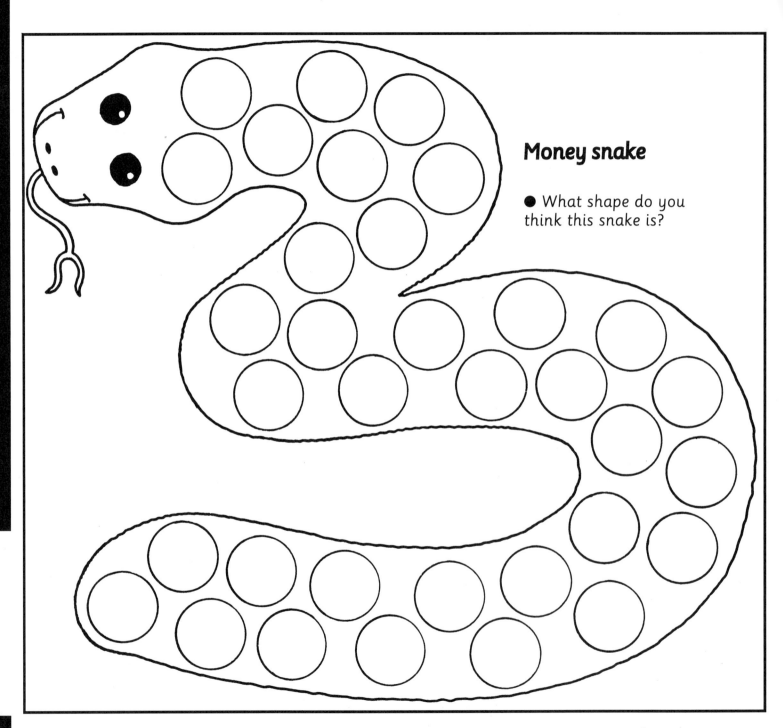

Money snake

● What shape do you think this snake is?

impact MATHS HOMEWORK

My favourite circle

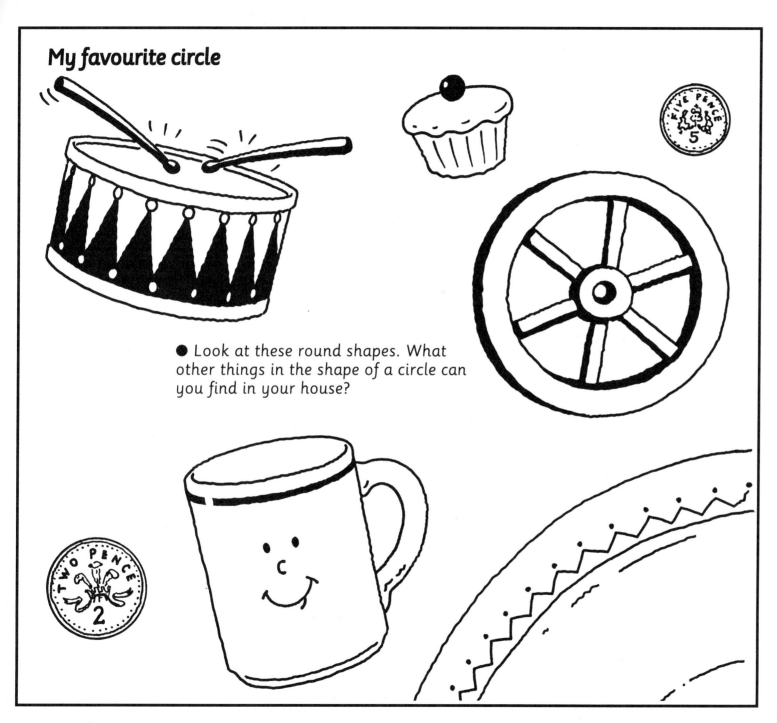

● Look at these round shapes. What other things in the shape of a circle can you find in your house?

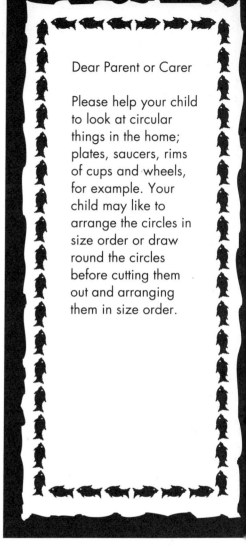

Dear Parent or Carer

Please help your child to look at circular things in the home; plates, saucers, rims of cups and wheels, for example. Your child may like to arrange the circles in size order or draw round the circles before cutting them out and arranging them in size order.

_____and

child

_____

helper(s)

_____

did this activity together

Teachers' Notes
FOUR YEAR OLDS

Coin jar Make three jars in the nursery or playgroup. How many coins can the children collect in each one? Perhaps when they have ten of each they can buy some biscuits for the whole nursery. Talk about the other coins. Lay them in a row according to their value. Which coin is worth the most?

Dough numerals Make huge and colourful numerals to stick on the walls. The children can stick the correct number of decorations on each numeral, for example, one piece of tinsel on the 1, two shiny stars on the 2 and so on. Show the children how to draw the numerals, starting at the top. Give the children some numerals (not too small) which are drawn in pencil so that they can draw over them in felt-tipped pen.

Numbered animals Let the children draw a long line of animals and put them on the wall. Number them 1st to 10th. Talk about the idea of a place in a line. Line up the children and talk about which place they are in the line. Look at the pages in the book and talk about the first page, the second page and so on.

Facial features The children may like to make faces using paper plates. These may be decorated with features and hair to resemble their owners. Encourage the children to arrange themselves into sets such as boys/girls; those wearing trousers/those not wearing trousers; those with blue eyes/those not with blue eyes and so on.

The noisy game Play this game in class. Make a new large floor track where the children use themselves as counters. They can throw the dice and count around the track, moving themselves as they do this. Write different actions in each space to make the game fun. For example, jump up and down three times, hop twice and so on.

Making numbers up! The children can make numbers in class. Make huge and colourful numerals to stick on the walls of the nursery. Use the right number of things to make each numeral – for example, one thing for '1', two for '2' and so on. Talk about how to draw the numerals – starting at the top. Give the children some numerals (not too small!) which are drawn in pencil that they can draw over in felt-tipped pen.

As long as my shoe How many things did each child need to make a line as long as their shoe. Draw around each child's foot, cut out the foot shape and write the number of things needed on it. Now make a pictograph of the numbers of things needed by sticking their 'feet' in the appropriate column – for example, the ones with a three on above the '3'. Make lines as long as their feet using things from around the classroom. How many do they use this time?

One more than... The children can practise playing this 'on the rug'. The teacher holds up three things and then asks, 'What's one more than this?'

The children have to tell her. She then adds one more object and they all count to see if they were right. Try 'two more than', if the children are finding this easy!

Wrong number! The children can do some more of these in class. Help them to count accurately by pointing at or touching the pictures as they count them. Ask the children to lay out the correct number of things in numbered sets. For example, if they have a set numbered 4, they must find four things. Give them sets with as large a number as they can manage.

Snakey! Display all the children's snakes. Make a really long and wonderful snake in school using twists of paper joined together with staples (like a series of toffees!). How many segments are there in this snake? What is the longest snake they can make? Can the children find three things which are shorter than their shortest snake and three things which are longer?

Heavy spoonful Discuss with the children how big things can be light and small things can be heavy. Bring in some examples of your own. For example, a large soft teddy is light, while a small weight may be heavy. Display their spoon pictures in two sets – light and heavy. Talk about the heaviest spoonfuls and the lightest.

Big spoon, small hand Try taking handfuls of small objects (for example, LEGO bricks or counters) and guessing how many there are. Count carefully, touching each brick as you count it. How many handfuls make up a jug or a mugful? Guess first and then count. How much bigger is the teacher's handful than the child's?

Favourite hour Make a series of clocks and put them on the wall, each one with the hands pointing to a different hour of the day. Write or draw the digital display for each hour underneath the clock. Now mount the children's drawings under the appropriate hour. Are there any times which have no drawings? Are there some times of the day which lots of people liked? Which is the teacher's favourite time of day and why?

impact MATHS HOMEWORK

Make a clock The children can make a large clock in class and display it on the wall. Each of them can paint or colour a different number? Draw the digital displays beside each number. Talk about the big hand and the little hand on the clock and discuss their different speeds of movement around the face.

Weekending! Display the children's drawings in different sets according to their content. Who was playing a sport? Who was watching TV? Discuss the sorts of things that people do at the weekend – for example, lying in and not having to get up in the morning! Talk about which days are weekend and which are weekdays. Rehearse the days of the week by saying them in unison.

Seasonal presents Make four large sets out of paper and pin them up on the wall. Ask the children to draw their presents and place them in the right sets. Talk about the weather in each season. Which season is the hottest? Which is the coolest? Write all the children's names on pieces of paper and ask them to place them in the sets according to the season in which their birthday falls.

The four game Set up a table; everything on the table must be in groups of four. Can the children arrange themselves in groups of four and sing a song? For example:

Four fat sausages sizzling in the pan,
If one goes pop and the other goes
  bang,
There will be two fat sausages sizzling
  in the pan.
Two fat sausages sizzling in the pan, ...

The five game Hands have five digits. The children can draw round their hands and colour each digit using a different colour. Then the numbers 1 to 5 can be written or stuck on to each digit. The children could play 'Five currant buns in a baker's shop'. They could make the buns, which could then be put on plates in fives.

Family order The children could arrange teddies, dollies and so on in order. The language of size is difficult for children (larger, shorter, wider, narrower). They should experience ordering using many different adjectives.

Feely bag game Encourage the children to describe the coins. For example, a £1 coin is golden, small, thick and heavy. Then they can then play this game using all of the coins.

Sorting coins You will need a coin dice, a selection of coins and a picture of a beetle for each child. Each beetle body part should have a different coin value. Let the children take turns at throwing the dice. The first child to cover their beetle with the correct coins is the winner.

Arranging pennies Make a display. This should include the word and symbol for 4. Ask each child to collect/make/paint four similar objects to display on the '4 table'.

Penny numbers The children could all draw a face. Each child could then see how many 1p coins will fit on to their face pictures. Can they arrange these in size order, beginning with the face with the least number of coins? How many children

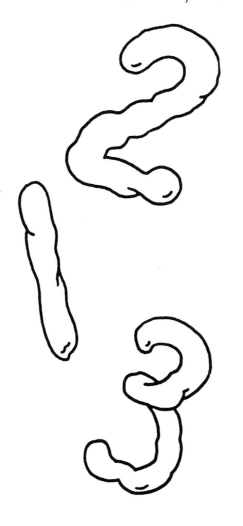

have the same number of coins on their picture as each other?

Hide the money This activity is excellent for encouraging mental dexterity. It can be repeated in the classroom situation with a small group of children. Place five 1p coins on to the carpet. Ask all the children except one to turn around. This child removes some coins and asks the other children to turn around and say how many coins are missing. Continue until each child has had a turn.

Ladybird Make a large display to illustrate the poem 'Ladybird, ladybird'. The children could hang their ladybirds as mobiles. Give them time to explain how they arranged the spots and how they overcame the problem of the seventh spot.

Witches' hats The children may like to cut out witch shapes suitable for placing their hats on. Their witches could then be arranged to make a number picture, for example, 'Five witches flew at night – one fell off her broomstick then there were four, Four witches flew at night...'. Ask the children for suggestions.

Different shapes The children may like to draw round a variety of shapes to create interesting patterns, for example, trains, cats and so on. Give each child time to explain which shapes are in their picture.

Make a hexagon The children may like to create a big patchwork quilt to show their tessellating hexagons. Alternatively, flowers could be made using a central hexagon and six surrounding hexagons. This could form part of a display showing the garden of 'Mary, Mary quite contrary'.

_____and

child

_____

helper(s)

_____

did this activity together

Coin jar

YOU WILL NEED: three small jars or pots or boxes, some paper to stick round them and some sticky tape, a few bright felt-tipped pens and some 1p, 2p and 5p coins.

You are going to decorate each jar with a particular coin, and then collect that coin in that jar.

● Draw round the 1p several times on one of the pieces of paper. Colour them in. Write the number 1 on the coins you have drawn. Do the same using another piece of paper for the 2p, and then for the 5p.

● Stick each piece of paper round one of your jars or boxes.

● Put the right coins in the right jars. Keep collecting them!

impact MATHS HOMEWORK

Dough numerals

● Can you make the numbers from 1 to 4 out of dough?

How to make dough:

1 cup of flour
Half a cup of salt
1 teaspoon cream of tartar
1 dessert spoon of oil
1 cup of water
Food colouring

Mix all the ingredients in a pan over a low heat, stirring all the time. Turn out on to a table and knead well.

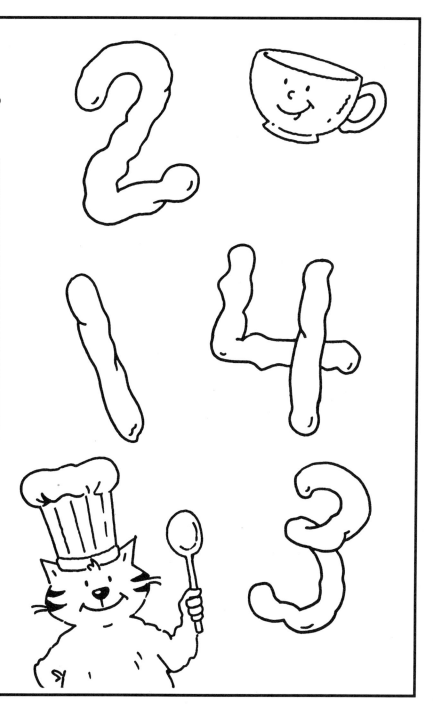

Dear Parent or Carer

Help your child to make the numerals out of dough. Perhaps they can make the right number of things – for example, four snakes – to go with each number?

_____and

child

_____

helper(s)

_____

did this activity together

_____and

child

_____

helper(s)

_____

did this activity together

Numbered animals

● Choose your three favourite animals. Imagine that they have come first, second and third in a race!

● Draw each animal below the right number. For example, if the giraffe came first, draw it below the '1st'.

Facial features

- Look at these pictures.
- How many heads can you see?
- How many open eyes?
- How many noses?
- How many ears?

Dear Parent or Carer

Can your child count the heads in your family? How about noses, mouths, ears and eyes? This game can be extended to legs, feet, hands, arms, knees, elbows and shoulders. Small children find it great fun practising counting and realising that the answers are the same. Extend the game by asking how many eyes are open and how many are closed. Are there more eyes open or more closed?

_____and

child

_____

helper(s)

_____

did this activity together

Dear Parent or Carer

This game – apart from being fun – helps children to practise counting as they go, so they must count the number of dots on the dice, and then count round the track. They also have to count noises!

_____and

child

_____

helper(s)

_____

did this activity together

The noisy game

YOU WILL NEED: a counter each, a dice and a noisy helper!!

● Take it in turns to throw the dice, and count that number of spaces around the track.

● Make the noise it says on the space you land on. The first person to have to make a particular noise three times is the winner!

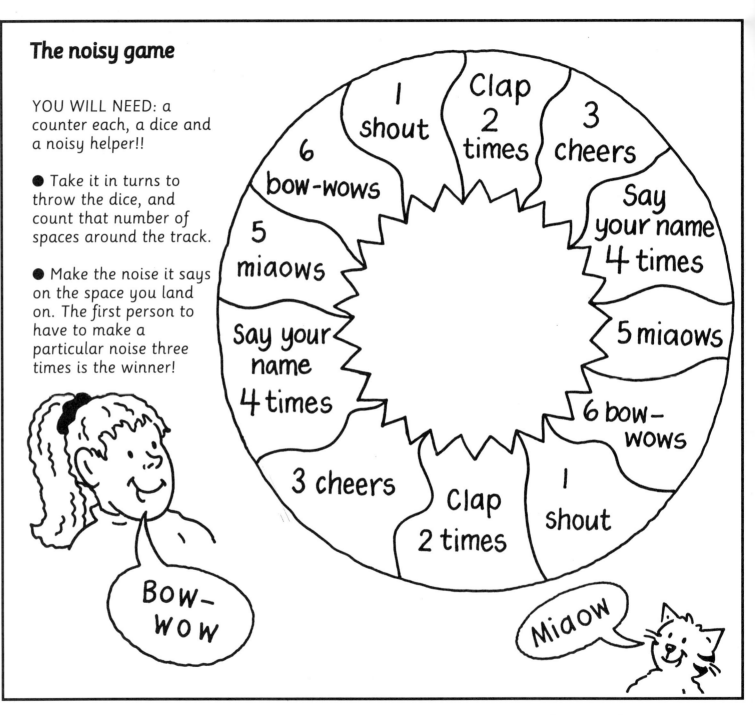

Making numbers up!

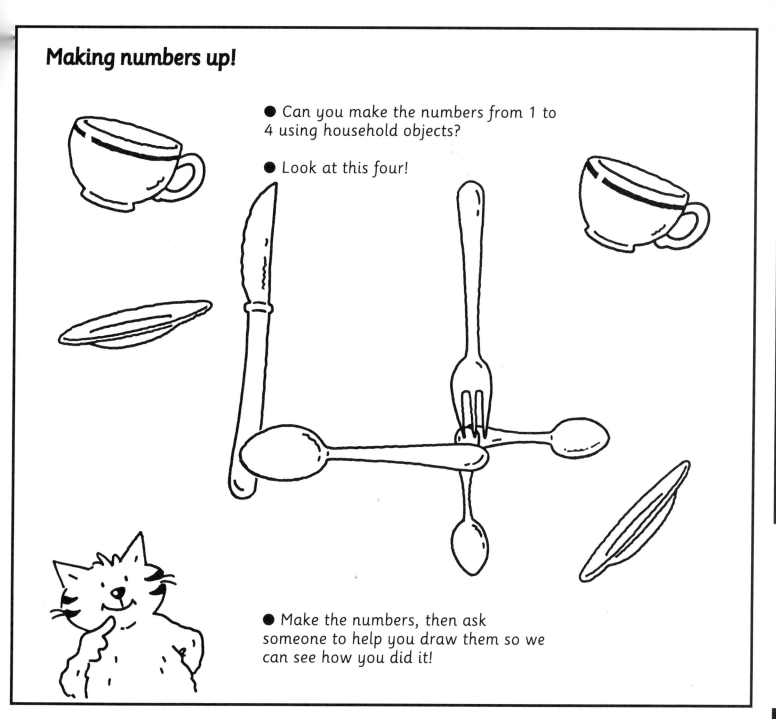

- Can you make the numbers from 1 to 4 using household objects?

- Look at this four!

- Make the numbers, then ask someone to help you draw them so we can see how you did it!

Dear Parent or Carer

This activity helps your child to concentrate on what the numerals look like. It reinforces children's recognition of the different numbers.

_____and

child

_____

helper(s)

_____

did this activity together

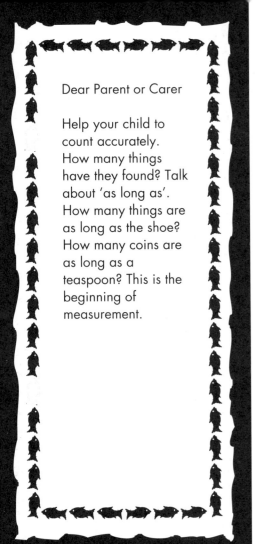

Dear Parent or Carer

Help your child to count accurately. How many things have they found? Talk about 'as long as'. How many things are as long as the shoe? How many coins are as long as a teaspoon? This is the beginning of measurement.

_____and

child

_____

helper(s)

_____

did this activity together

As long as my shoe

● Ask someone to help you draw round your shoe.

● Now find as many very small things as you can and lay them in a line. You are trying to make a line which is as long as your shoe!

● How many things did you need?

One more than...

- Find a number of things, for example, three toy cars.

- Ask your helper how many there are. They must tell you, for example, 'Three.'

- They then ask you how many one more is.

- You tell them what you think one more is, for example, 'Four.'

- Take one more. Now count. Were you right?

- Do this again several times. How many times are you right?

Dear Parent or Carer

This is a very helpful way to get children to think about one more than. They have to work it out in their heads and then check it. Help them by making it as much fun as possible! Make the numbers larger if they are finding it too easy.

_____and

child

_____

helper(s)

_____

did this activity together

_____and

child

_____

helper(s)

_____

did this activity together

Wrong number!

These sets have been drawn with the wrong number of things in them.

● Can you make them right by drawing some more things in each set?

Snakey!

● Ask someone to help you make two snakes! You can make them out of anything you like – strips of paper coloured in, string threaded with bottle tops or dried pasta, wool, or anything else you can think of – BUT – one snake **must** be longer than the other!

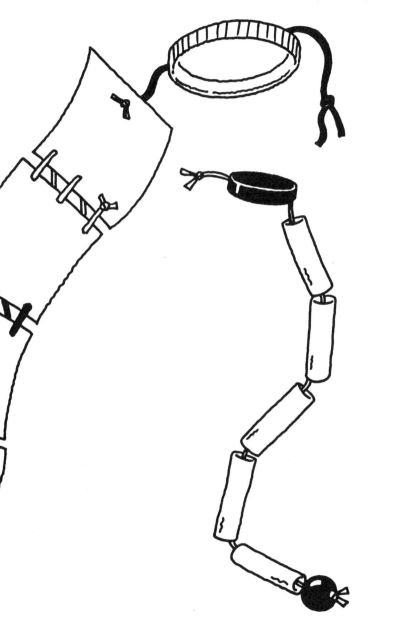

_____and

child

_____

helper(s)

_____

did this activity together

_____and
child

_____
helper(s)

_____

did this activity together

Heavy spoonful

YOU WILL NEED: two large spoons about the same size.

● Find something to put on one of the spoons which is very heavy.

● Find something to put on the other spoon which is very light.

● Lay the two spoons beside each other. Draw round each one carefully, and ask your helper to label the spoons and their contents. Bring your drawing into school.

Big spoon, small hand

YOU WILL NEED: dried lentils or pasta or rice or sugar.

● Find the largest spoon you can.

● Which do you think holds more, your hand or a big spoon?

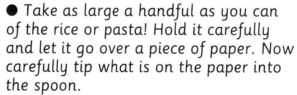

● Take as large a handful as you can of the rice or pasta! Hold it carefully and let it go over a piece of paper. Now carefully tip what is on the paper into the spoon.

● Does it fit? Is there space for more?

● Which held more? Draw the one which held the most – either your hand or the spoon. Bring your drawing into school.

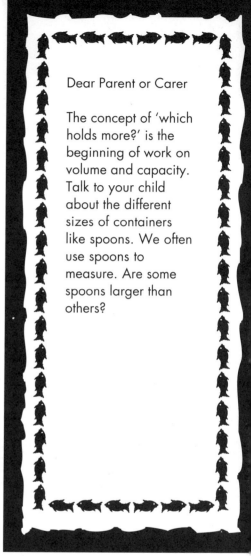

Dear Parent or Carer

The concept of 'which holds more?' is the beginning of work on volume and capacity. Talk to your child about the different sizes of containers like spoons. We often use spoons to measure. Are some spoons larger than others?

_____and

child

_____

helper(s)

_____

did this activity together

Favourite hour

● Have you got a favourite time of day?

● Talk to someone about what time this is.

● Look at the pictures below. With your helper, draw the hands on the clock and the numbers on the digital display to show your favourite time.

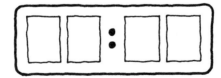

● Draw a picture of what you do at your favourite time today in the space opposite.

Make a clock

● Make a clock using some numbers written on small pieces of paper or card, and a fork and a teaspoon for the hands. Lay your clock out on the kitchen table.

● Cut out the small digital displays from below.

● Take it in turns with someone to place one next to the right number on the clock, for example the 3.00 display goes next to the 3 on the clock.

● As you place the label there, make the hands say 3 o'clock. Do this for all the labels.

Dear Parent or Carer

This activity is designed to help children to relate the digital times to the hands on the clock face. Talk about these times. Can they think of things which are happening at each time?

_____and

child

_____

helper(s)

_____

did this activity together

Dear Parent or Carer

Talk about the days of the week. Which are weekdays and which are weekends? Every now and again, say all the days of the week in order, so that your child gets used to hearing them.

_____and

child

_____

helper(s)

_____

did this activity together

Weekending!

● What happens at the weekend which does not happen in the week?

● Think of three things which happen or which you do at the weekend, which do not occur on week days.

● Draw a picture of these three things in the space below. Ask someone to write what they are.

impact MATHS HOMEWORK

Seasonal presents

Imagine that you have to give someone a present for each season!

● What would be a good winter present?

● What would be a good summer present?

Summer

Spring

Winter

Autumn

● Think of a present for each season. It could be something you would like!

● Ask someone to write each present you think of in the box labelled for that season. Draw a picture of your favourite present.

Dear Parent or Carer

Talk about the seasons with your child. Which months go in each season? Which seasons are coldest and which are warmest? Talk about the sorts of things which happen in each season – leaves falling and so on.

_____and

child

_____

helper(s)

_____

did this activity together

Dear Parent or Carer

Encourage your child to trace over the number 4, beginning at the top. This game will help your child to recognise and write the symbol for four and pick up four objects quickly. Encourage your child to pick up four LEGO bricks from the pile without counting but looking carefully first.

_____and

child

_____

helper(s)

_____

did this activity together

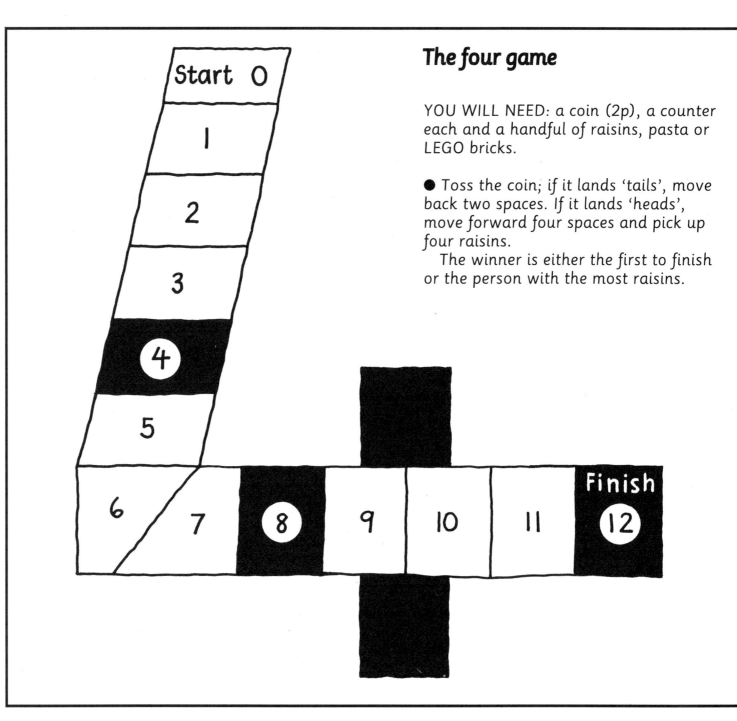

The four game

YOU WILL NEED: a coin (2p), a counter each and a handful of raisins, pasta or LEGO bricks.

● Toss the coin; if it lands 'tails', move back two spaces. If it lands 'heads', move forward four spaces and pick up four raisins.
   The winner is either the first to finish or the person with the most raisins.

impact MATHS HOMEWORK

The five game

YOU WILL NEED: a coin (5p), a counter each and a handful of raisins, pasta or LEGO bricks.

● Take turns to toss the 5p coin. If it lands 'tails', move back two spaces. If it lands 'heads', move forward five spaces and pick up five raisins.

The winner is either the first to finish or the person with the most raisins.

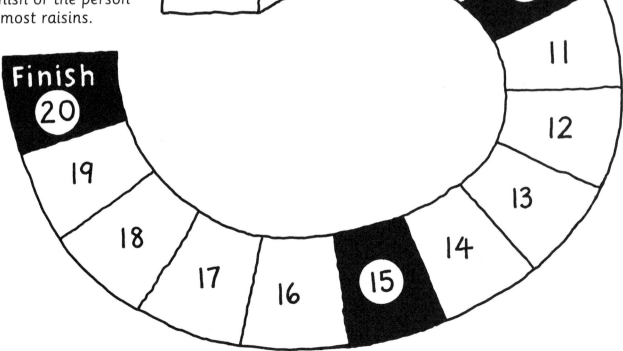

Dear Parent or Carer

Encourage your child to trace over the 5 in two movements. First, make this shape $\int$, then finish the number 5 off with a second movement – the stroke on top, 5.

Can your child try to predict which number the counter will land on? Talk to them about the numbers on the track. Can your child point to number 4? Which number is one more and/or one less than 4?

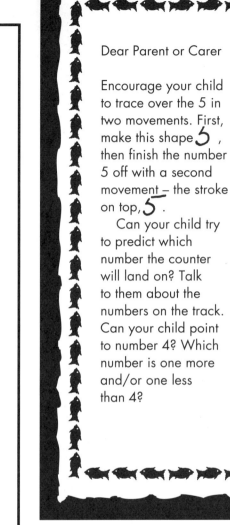

_____and

child

_____

helper(s)

_____

did this activity together

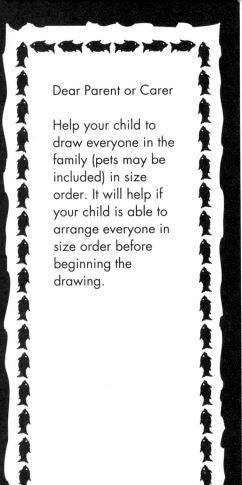
Family order

Mummy

● Who is the shortest here?

Jo-Jo

Gus

Teddy

Larkin

● Can you arrange this family in height order?

impact MATHS HOMEWORK

Feely bag game

YOU WILL NEED: some 2p and 1p coins and a paper bag.

● Put your hand inside the feely bag. Pick up a coin and guess if it is a 1p or a 2p.

● Take it out of the bag to see if you are right.

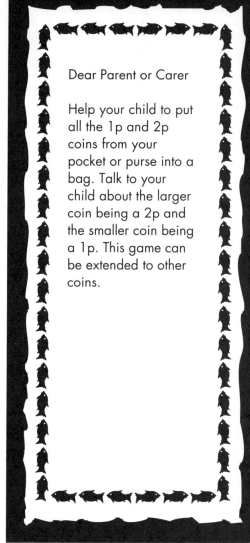

Dear Parent or Carer

Help your child to put all the 1p and 2p coins from your pocket or purse into a bag. Talk to your child about the larger coin being a 2p and the smaller coin being a 1p. This game can be extended to other coins.

_____and

child

_____

helper(s)

_____

did this activity together

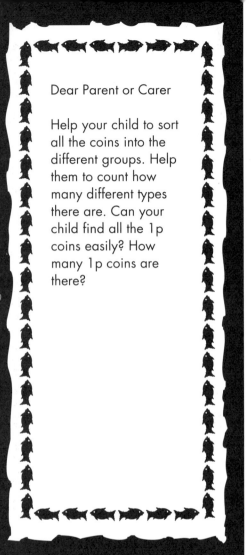

_____and

child

_____

helper(s)

_____

did this activity together

Sorting coins

YOU WILL NEED: some 1p, 2p, 5p, 10p, 20p and 50p coins.

● Sort your coins into these groups:

bronze/not bronze   **smooth edge/not smooth edge**

silver/not silver   **round/not round**

Arranging pennies

● How many different ways can you arrange four pence?

Dear Parent or Carer

Ask your child to identify and collect all the 1p coins from your pocket or purse. Help your child to collect four and place them on the coin drawings. Encourage your child to point to each coin when counting.

_____and

child

_____

helper(s)

_____

did this activity together

_____and

child

_____

helper(s)

_____

did this activity together

Penny numbers

● How many 1p coins will fit on to the number 4 below?

Hide the money

YOU WILL NEED: *five 1p coins, a saucer and a cup.*

● Look carefully at the 1p coins on the saucer.

● Ask your helper to put some of the coins under the cup while you look away.

● Can you say how many 1p coins are under the cup?

● Now you put some of the 1p coins under the cup and ask your helper to say how many are missing from the saucer.

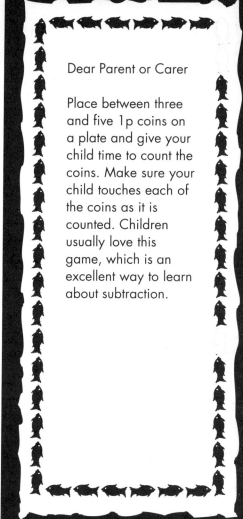

Dear Parent or Carer

Place between three and five 1p coins on a plate and give your child time to count the coins. Make sure your child touches each of the coins as it is counted. Children usually love this game, which is an excellent way to learn about subtraction.

_____and

child

_____

helper(s)

_____

did this activity together

Ladybird

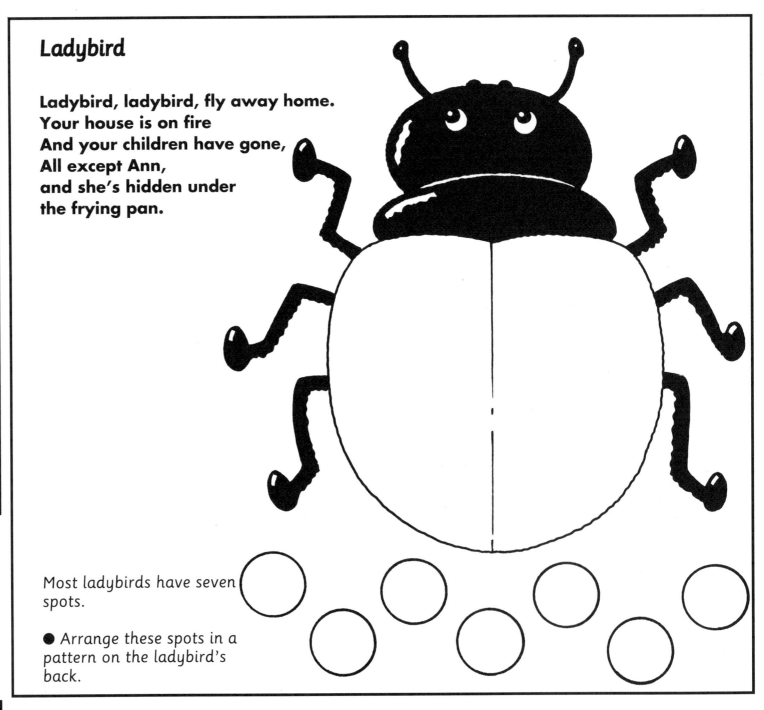

Ladybird, ladybird, fly away home.
Your house is on fire
And your children have gone,
All except Ann,
and she's hidden under
the frying pan.

Most ladybirds have seven spots.

● Arrange these spots in a pattern on the ladybird's back.

Witches' hats

● Can you make a witch's hat for teddy?

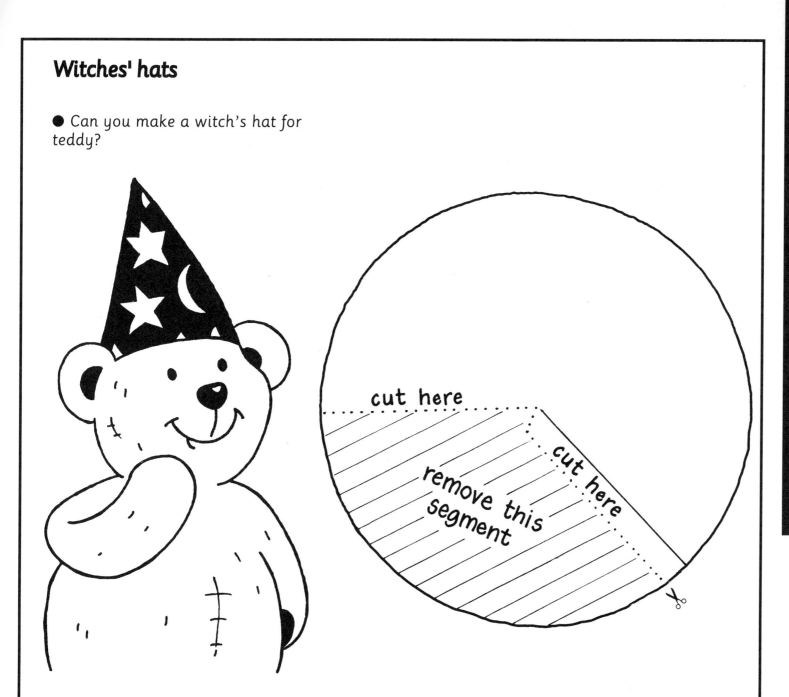

cut here

cut here

remove this segment

Dear Parent or Carer

Help your child to cut out the circle and remove the segment. Stick the two straight edges together to make a cone shape. Your child may like to decorate the hat with pictures.

_____and

child

_____

helper(s)

_____

did this activity together

_____and

child

_____

helper(s)

_____

did this activity together

Different shapes

● How many of these shapes can you find in your house and also outside? Name some of these things.

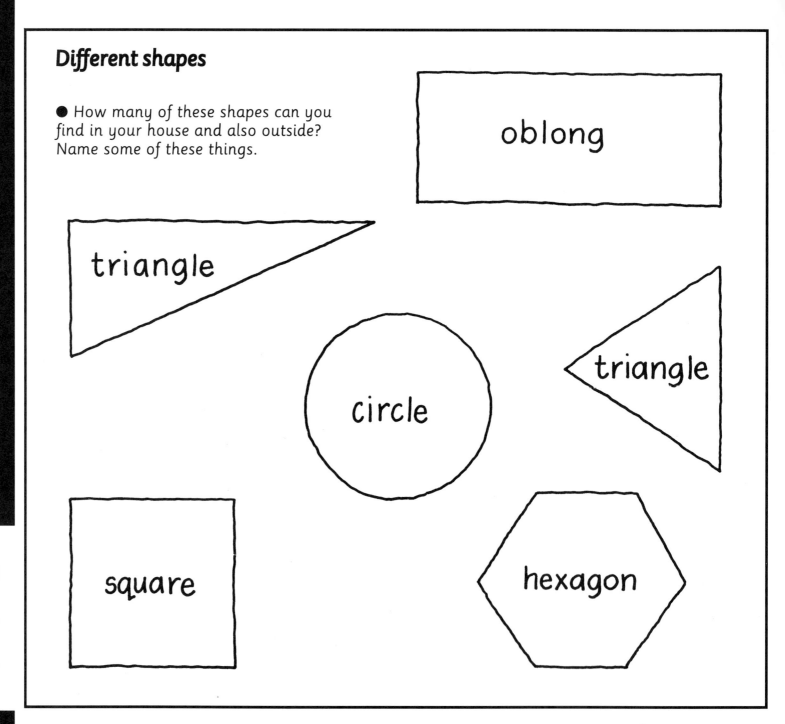

impact MATHS HOMEWORK

Make a hexagon

● Colour, then carefully cut out, these six triangles.

● Ask someone to help you arrange the six triangles into a hexagon shape.

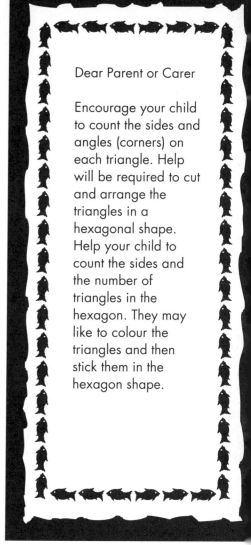

Dear Parent or Carer

Encourage your child to count the sides and angles (corners) on each triangle. Help will be required to cut and arrange the triangles in a hexagonal shape. Help your child to count the sides and the number of triangles in the hexagon. They may like to colour the triangles and then stick them in the hexagon shape.

_____and

child

_____

helper(s)

_____

did this activity together

Teachers' Notes
FIVE YEAR OLDS

Drawing numbers The children can practise drawing numerals in class. Give them lightly drawn pencil numerals which they can draw over in felt-tipped pen. Emphasise that they must start at the top of the numeral. Then they can match their finished numerals to the correct number of sweets or raisins – as a reward!

Steps Make this game for the children to play in class. Perhaps it can go up to ten? Can they invent their own game where you have to do an action when you land on each square? For example, you might have to bow, or salute, or bark like a dog. Can they play this game backwards – counting down instead of up?!

Washing line Make a large and colourful washing line of numbers for the class. Use it to count along. Write the numbers on the front and back of the pieces of paper – also write the names of those who are four years old on the '4', and all those who are five on the '5' and so on. The children can count in unison as you point to the numbers. Then point to any number and ask them what it is!

Coin fingers Talk about the different coins. Lay out the number of 1p coins the children would need to make the same value as the 5p coin. Ask them to arrange the coins in sets – for example, a pile of five 1p coins, a 5p, and two 2ps and a 1p piled up. All these are the same value. Talk about the 10p coin. Make a line of all the coins in value order and talk about the fact that the £1 coin is worth the most.

Animal ladder Make a ladder for the classroom. Use teddy bears or other soft toys to put one animal on each rung. Talk about which toy is on the first rung, which is on the second and so on. Working in groups of five or six, give each child a numeral and ask them to get in line by calling out 'first, second' and so on. Use these terms in order that the children associate these with the correct numeral.

How much is your foot worth? The children may like to repeat this activity in school using a strip of paper that fits around their head. Do all the headbands 'cost' the same amount? Who has the most expensive and cheapest headband? What about the dollies' and teddies' headbands?

Finger counting Practise counting on fingers. Practise starting with a number that we 'hold in our heads' and then counting on. For example, I hold five in my head and count on three – 'six, seven, eight' – holding up one finger for each number spoken. This is a really useful skill later on.

Age labels The children can display all their labels in appropriate sets – for example, those that are a single digit, those which begin with a '1' (such as 15), those that begin with a '2' and so on. You may need nine sets! Talk about the fifty numbers as beginning with five, the seventy numbers as beginning with seven and so on.

Alphabet number patterns Display each child's name, nicely written by them. (You can always write it very faintly in pencil so that they can go over the letters in felt-tipped pen). Display the 'value' of each letter by drawing dots underneath it, and stretch a string from the name to the amount the name adds up to. Several names will then be attached to each amount! This makes a lovely display.

Buy your name The children can display their names in the class with a piece of ribbon or string attached to the amount each name adds up to. The amounts should be displayed by sticking actual coins on the wall with sticky tape. This will help to emphasise the coins needed to make up that amount of money. Whose name is worth the most? Whose is worth the least?

One more please! The children can create a large track game to play in class where they are the counters moving along the track. Large bricks, cars or teddies can be piled beside each space on the track to be the things they take! Make sure that several spaces have a star – so they have to take 'one more'. Practise counting 'one more than' 'on the rug'. For example, say, 'Three' and the children must say what is one more than that.

One less! Practise playing this game 'on the rug'. One child holds up a few of their fingers. The children all count them. (Counting together out loud helps to reinforce this skill.) Then the child asks, 'What is one less?' and the other children must guess. Proceed to two less or to using bigger numbers if the children find this easy.

Stripy tiger! Look around for instances of things with stripes. Collect as many as you can. Then make a pictograph by drawing pictures of all the things you have found with stripes on them on to small oblong pieces of paper, and sticking these on a graph above the number which represents the number of stripes they have. What has the most stripes and what has the least?

Birthday card The children can display all their lovely cards. Do all the cards say the same number? Which ones say the smaller number? Which say the larger number? Display them in two (or three) sets. The children can practise drawing numerals in class. Give them lightly drawn pencil numerals which they can draw over in felt-tip. Emphasise that they must start at the top of the numeral.

Which number? This is an excellent game to play 'on the rug'. The children can think about which numbers are bigger than five, and which are smaller. You will need a number line (see 'Washing line', page 62) to refer to and to help them see which numbers are bigger or smaller. Encourage questions about the shape of the numeral – for example, 'Is the number drawn with straight lines?'

Coins around a mug Discuss the different coins which were used. Make a line of all the coins along the wall (you will need to stick each coin up under sticky tape) and make sure they go in order of value from the £1 to the 1p. Discuss what you can buy with each coin. Talk about the distance round the mug. Measure round a mug or a beaker with string in school and count how many bricks fit along the string.

Knee high! Compare the lengths of the pieces of string. Which is longest, and which is shortest? Arrange them in a 'string graph' in order of length. Can the children draw round their hand (fingers closed!) and put a piece of string around that. Is this piece of string longer or shorter than the one which went round their foot?

Fat toy, thin toy Talk about 'fat' and 'thin'. Choose a fat object in the classroom and put a piece of string round it! Guess how many bricks (large ones!) will fit along the piece of string. Now choose a thin object. Measure it in the same way. How many bricks more go round the fat one? Find out by building two towers, one next to the other.

Lighting up time Make four large sets out of paper and pin them up on the wall. Write the 'lighting up times' in each season. Talk about the lengths of the days in each season and the weather. Which season is the hottest? Which is the coolest? Write all the children's names on pieces of paper and ask them to place them in the sets according to the season in which their birthday falls.

How long did I take? Discuss how long different children took to get a 4. Play the game again in class, timing how long it takes to get a different number – for example, a 6. Does it make any difference which number they choose. Talk about how long five minutes is and how much around the clock the big hand has to move.

Seasonal sort-out Make a list of the months of the year in class and sort them into the seasons. Talk about whether everybody agreed about which months

were in which season. Write all the children's names on pieces of paper. Ask them to place them in sets according to the season in which their birthday falls.

Day count! Arrange the days of the week in a vertical chart from longest to shortest –
Friday 6 letters
Monday 6 letters
Sunday 6 letters
Tuesday 7 letters
Thursday 8 letters
Saturday 8 letters
Wednesday 9 letters
Rehearse the correct order of the days of the week by chanting them in unison.

Snowflake pattern These snowflakes could be threaded and hung as mobiles from the ceiling. The children could be asked how many parts there were after the first fold and then after the second fold. You may like to introduce the words: half, quarter and so on.

Pasta patterns For this follow-up activity you will need a supply of coloured cubes. Make a simple pattern, for example, one red, one yellow, one blue. Can all the children take turns to predict and place a cube to continue the repeating pattern?

Ten fat sausages The children can be arranged in lines of ten. Any extra children can use percussion to be the pop or bang. The children can sing and act the song. It may help if the children stand in a line and hold numbers in this arrangement: 10, 8, 6, 4, 2, 1, 3, 5, 7, 9. Other singing games could be played, including 'Ten green bottles' or 'There were ten in a bed'.

Clapping names Are all the children able to clap their names? Can they arrange

themselves in clapping families? They may like to use percussion to tap out the syllables in other familiar words, for example, el–e–phant.

Design a patchwork quilt Display the children's work around a patchwork picture that they have created. They may be able to visit a church or a Victorian building or other places of interest to give them ideas for their design.

Sorting leaves The children could work in small groups of no more than about eight. Each child could be given a different leaf. Encourage the children to describe their leaf using several of the adjectives used in the task. The children could then be asked to sort the leaves into two sets using one of the criteria for sorting.

How many legs? You will need a collection of vehicles for this sorting activity. Each child chooses a vehicle and then attempts to find other children with the same wheel number as their own. This will generate lots of descriptive conversation.

Play the money game This is an excellent game to play in spare moments. It can easily be adapted – the children may like to suggest ways of spending or saving to create new challenges.

Long caterpillar Can the children design a different patterned snake using 1p and 2p coins? For example, 2p, 2p, 1p, 2p, 2p, 1p and so on. How many different patterns can they generate? Encourage the children to take turns continuing the patterns. Ask questions, for example, 'Which coin comes next?'

Box shapes The children may like to arrange themselves into families around

particular shaped boxes, for example, four oblong and two square faced box. How many children are there in each set? Can the children make a box, using Polydron or a similar construction kit, the same as the one that they had brought?

Going shopping It would be excellent to have a class shop selling toys. Encourage the children to write price labels (no more than 10p). Limit them to 2p and 1p coins so that they can calculate accurately the amount needed for the transactions.

Make a cuboid The children may like to estimate how many wooden bricks will fit into various cuboid boxes or containers. Can they estimate about how many will fit on to the bottom of the box? Care will need to be exercised about the relative sizes of box and brick.

Beautiful butterfly Blot paintings and string pulling pictures create wonderful symmetrical patterns. Children are fascinated and surprised by their results. The children could cut simple pictures of teddies, and such like, in half and attempt to draw the matching half.

Cylinders Give each child time to talk about their model and discuss how it works. If you have some large cylinders, they could move a fairly heavy object by using the cylinders as rollers under a short plank of wood.

Favourite car colours The children may like to draw and colour in their own car shapes. Let them sort these shapes into sets and display them on a Venn diagram. Talk about popular and unpopular colours and how many cars there are of each colour.

_____and

child

_____

helper(s)

_____

did this activity together

Drawing numbers

● Draw each of the numbers on this page as many times as you can. Start with your age. Always follow the arrows!

● Can you draw them by yourself? Draw a really big number on the back of this sheet and colour it in.

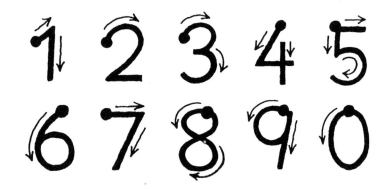

Steps

You are going to make a huge track game all across the floor!

YOU WILL NEED: six large pieces of paper – each one with a number drawn on it: 1, 2, 3, 4, 5, 6 – and a coin.

● Lay the pieces of paper in a line with spaces between them.

● Stand on any one of the numbers.

● Ask your helper to throw the coin. If it lands on 'heads', move on to the number below the one you are now on. If it lands on 'tails' move on to the number above the one you are now on. Say the name of the number out loud.

● Keep playing until you have stood on all six numbers!

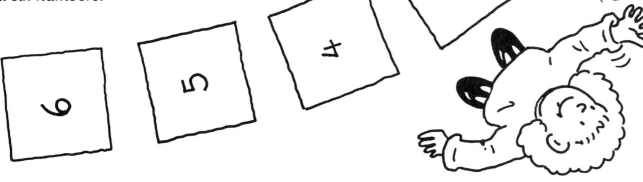

Dear Parent or Carer

This activity is to help children recognise the numbers up to 6 and to be able to count up to 6. It also helps them to realise the 'size' of the numbers – that is, that 4 is larger than 3 and so on.

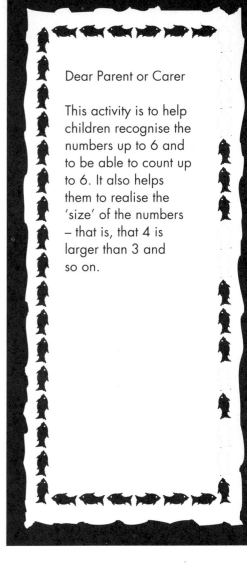

_____and

child

_____

helper(s)

_____

did this activity together

_____and

child

_____

helper(s)

_____

did this activity together

Washing line

YOU WILL NEED: a piece of wool or string hung up along the wall above where you sleep, eleven pieces of paper and some felt-tipped pens or paints to colour them.

● Draw '0' on the first piece of paper, draw '1' on the next one, and so on, up to 10. Under the numbers, draw that number of things, for example, under the 3 you could draw three cats, under the 4 you could draw four dinosaurs, and so on. On the one with 0, you don't draw anything.

● Hang all the pieces of paper, in order, along the line above your bed. (You can pin them up with clothes pegs!)

Coin fingers

- ● Ask someone to help you draw round your hands.

- ● Cover each finger with a line of coins! Use 1ps, 2ps or 5ps.

- ● How many coins do you use?

- ● Can you tell your helper which coin is worth the most? Which one is worth the least?

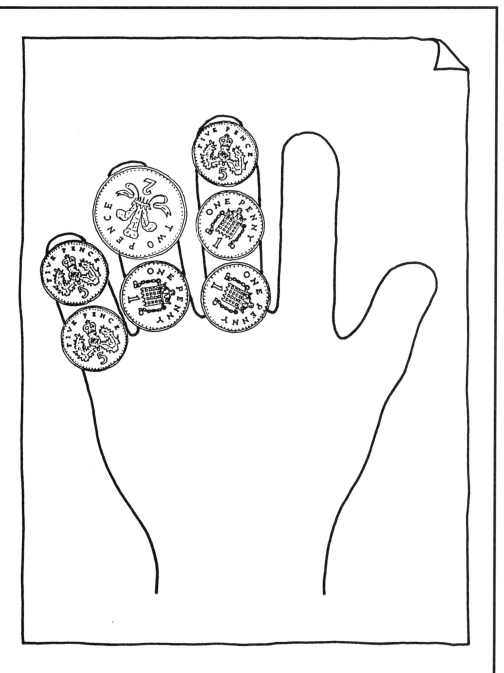

Dear Parent or Carer

Help your child to draw round their hand accurately. Help them to count the coins and discuss the fact that not all coins are worth the same amount. Write the numbers of coins on the hands so that they can bring their drawings of their hands into school.

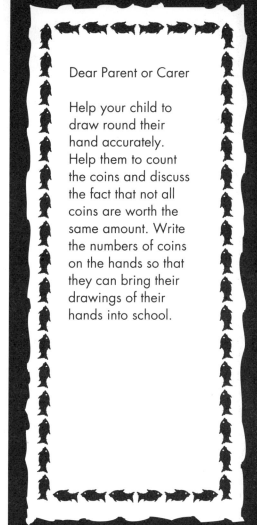

_____ and

child

_____

helper(s)

_____

did this activity together

Dear Parent or Carer

Which animal is on the first rung? Which animals are on the second rung and the third rung? Talk about the order of the animals. Which is the highest and which is the lowest? This will help reinforce the idea of order.

_____and

child

_____

helper(s)

_____

did this activity together

Animal ladder

● Can you think of five creatures which you see regularly? For example, they might be cats, dogs, goldfish, sheep or even spiders or worms. They are unlikely to be elephants or cobras unless you live near a zoo!

● Draw carefully, one animal on each rung of the ladder on the right.

● Bring your drawings into school.

How much is your foot worth?

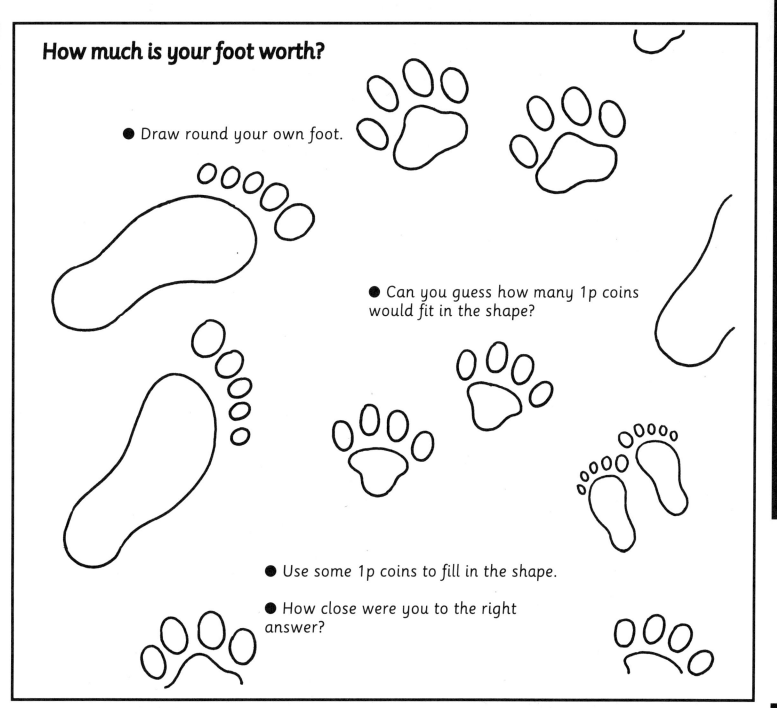

- Draw round your own foot.

- Can you guess how many 1p coins would fit in the shape?

- Use some 1p coins to fill in the shape.

- How close were you to the right answer?

Dear Parent or Carer

Give help with drawing around your child's foot. Can your child sort out the 1p coins from your pocket or purse? Help your child to arrange the coins so that they do not overlap or fall out of the foot shape. Encourage your child to touch and move each coin as they count. A possible extension to this game is for your child to try drawing round other feet in the family and finding out how much these feet are worth!

_____and

child

_____

helper(s)

_____

did this activity together

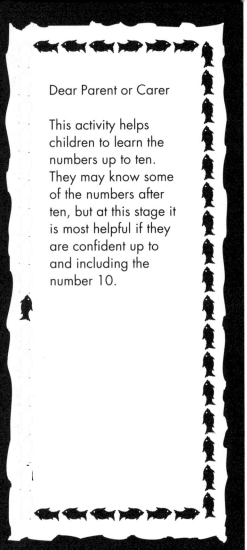

_____and

child

_____

helper(s)

_____

did this activity together

Finger counting

How far can you count on your fingers? You can count each finger once and get up to 10!

● Or you can count the knuckles (joints). How many does this mean you count up to?

● Count as far as you can on your fingers. Then ask someone to draw round both hands. Draw a hat on each finger and thumb and number the hats!

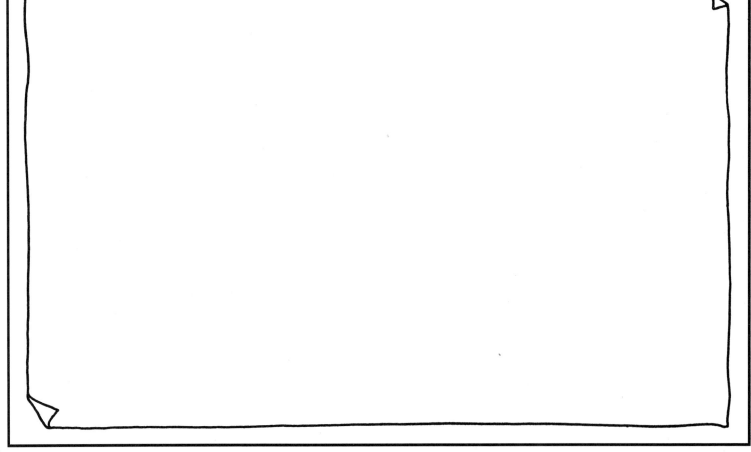

Age labels

● Make a label for everyone you live with which says their age on it.

● Draw something nice on each label and ask someone to help you write their age in numbers.

● Bring some or all of your labels into school if you like!

30 years old

5 years old

1½ years old

Dear Parent or Carer

This activity helps us to look at numbers above ten and talk about these. At this stage, we are not expecting children to count above ten, but we shall talk about the larger numbers and see how large they are.

_____and

child

_____

helper(s)

_____

did this activity together

Dear Parent or Carer

An example of this activity would look like this:

S o p h i e
1 3 1 2 3 2 = 12

This activity is a lot easier if you can draw dots beside or below the numbers – one dot beside 1, two dots beside 2 and so on. Then the child can count up all the dots. This is a big sum!

_____and

child

_____

helper(s)

_____

did this activity together

Alphabet number patterns

● With your helper go through the alphabet below and write the numbers 1, 2 and 3 below each letter in turn. For example, below 'a' write 1, below 'b' write 2, below 'c' write 3, below 'd' write 1, below 'e' write 2 and so on.

● When you have done this, write down your name. Write the letter numbers below the letters in your name. Ask your helper if they can help you to add up all the numbers to find out how much your name is worth!

a b c d e f g h i

1 2 3 _ _ _ _ _ _

j k l m n o p q r

_ _ _ _ _ _ _ _ _

s t u v w x w z

_ _ _ _ _ _ _

impact MATHS HOMEWORK

Buy your name

● Imagine that you are buying the letters to write your name. Letters in this game cost 2p for big letters, and 1p for little letters. For example, 'M' costs 2p and 'm' costs 1p.

● Ask someone to help you work out how much your name will cost to write. Bring your answer into school.

Letters for sale

2p

1p

Dear Parent or Carer

It will help the children if you can do this activity with real coins. Use 1p coins and help the children to add them up carefully.

_____and

child

_____

helper(s)

_____

did this activity together

_____and
child

_____
helper(s)

_____

did this activity together

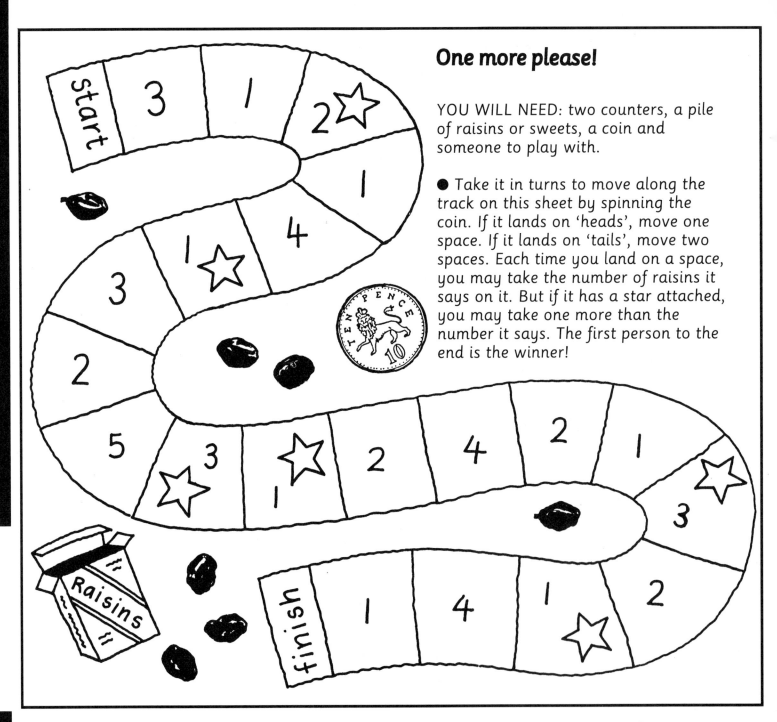

One more please!

YOU WILL NEED: two counters, a pile of raisins or sweets, a coin and someone to play with.

● Take it in turns to move along the track on this sheet by spinning the coin. If it lands on 'heads', move one space. If it lands on 'tails', move two spaces. Each time you land on a space, you may take the number of raisins it says on it. But if it has a star attached, you may take one more than the number it says. The first person to the end is the winner!

impact MATHS HOMEWORK

One less!

YOU WILL NEED: a pile of LEGO bricks or counters and someone to play with.

● Take it in turns to take a small pile of the LEGO bricks. You go first. Count out how many you have, then ask the other person, 'What is one less than this number?' If they can answer this question correctly, they take a brick to keep!

What is one less than this number?

● Now they get to take a handful of bricks and ask you the question, 'What's one less than?' If you can answer this correctly, you can keep a brick.

● Now it is your turn to take a handful of bricks. Play until one of you has five bricks!

Dear Parent or Carer

The question 'What's one less than?' is often much harder for children than the question, 'What's one more than?' This is because the latter question can be answered by counting, but 'What's one less than?' has to be answered by counting *back*! Help your child with this.

_____and

child

_____

helper(s)

_____

did this activity together

_____and

child

_____

helper(s)

_____

did this activity together

Stripy tiger!

● How many stripes can you count on the tiger?

● Can you draw a picture of any animal or toy or piece of clothing or piece of furniture which has stripes?

● Can you number the stripes along the bottom of the page?

Birthday card

● Can you invent a really good birthday card for yourself on your next birthday?

● Make sure you know how old you will be, then draw that number as big as you can on a folded piece of paper. Decorate it or draw a funny picture. Bring your card into school.

_____and

child

_____

helper(s)

_____

did this activity together

_____and

child

_____

helper(s)

_____

did this activity together

Which number?

- Think of a number between 1 and 12.

- Ask someone to guess which number you are thinking about.

- They may have three questions to help them guess, **but** you can only answer yes or no.

- Tell your helper that they can use one of the number strips below to help them. So, if they ask, 'Is it bigger than 5?' and you say 'No!' they can cross out the numbers 6, 7, 8, 9, 10, 11 and 12 because it cannot be one of those. Can they guess your number in only three questions?

- Then, they must think of a number and you can try to guess it by asking them three questions. You can use a number strip as well. Cross out all the numbers it cannot be.

1	2	3	4	5	6	7	8	9	10	11	12

1	2	3	4	5	6	7	8	9	10	11	12

Coins around a mug

YOU WILL NEED: a mug, a piece of paper, a pencil, some coins and someone to help you.

● Stand the mug on the piece of paper and draw carefully around it.

● Look at the circle you have drawn. How many coins do you think will fit all around it – guess, and ask your helper to guess too.

● Now lay coins in a ring all around your circle. How many fit?

● Put the coins in a line along the bottom of this page, and draw round them. Ask your helper to write the numbers on them all, or do it yourself. Bring your work into school.

Dear Parent or Carer

Measuring around things is quite a difficult thing for small children to do. They have to get the idea that the distance around something is still a 'length'. This activity also helps coin recognition. Talk about which coins they have used.

_____and

child

_____

helper(s)

_____

did this activity together

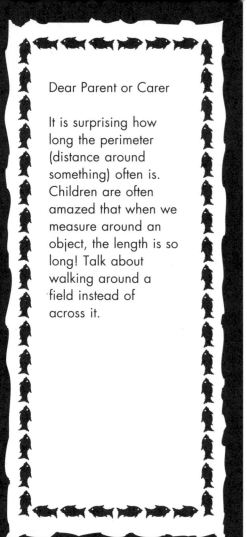

_____and

child

_____

helper(s)

_____

did this activity together

Knee high!

YOU WILL NEED: some paper and string and someone to help you.

● Draw carefully around your foot.

● Take a piece of string – it helps if it is slightly damp (not dripping wet!). Carefully lay the string over the outline of your foot. Cut it off to the right length, so that the piece of string goes exactly around the outline of your foot.

● Ask your helper to help you see if the piece of string which went all around your foot is longer or shorter than the height of your knee from the ground.

● Colour in your foot outline and bring it and your string into school.

impact MATHS HOMEWORK

Fat toy, thin toy

● Find your fattest toy. Find your thinnest toy.

● Using two pieces of string, measure round both of them. Gently wind one piece of string around the first toy (at its fattest part!). Cut the string to the right length. Do the same for the second toy at its thinnest part.

● How many times will the smaller piece of string fit along the bigger piece of string?

● Draw both toys carefully and bring the pictures and the strings into school.

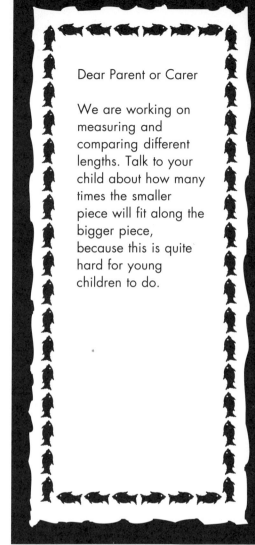

Dear Parent or Carer

We are working on measuring and comparing different lengths. Talk to your child about how many times the smaller piece will fit along the bigger piece, because this is quite hard for young children to do.

_____and

child

_____

helper(s)

_____

did this activity together

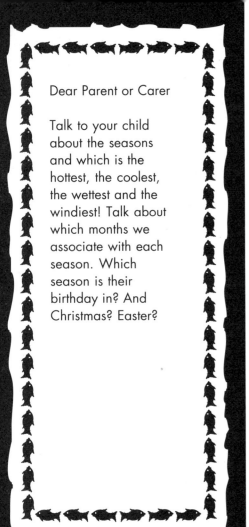
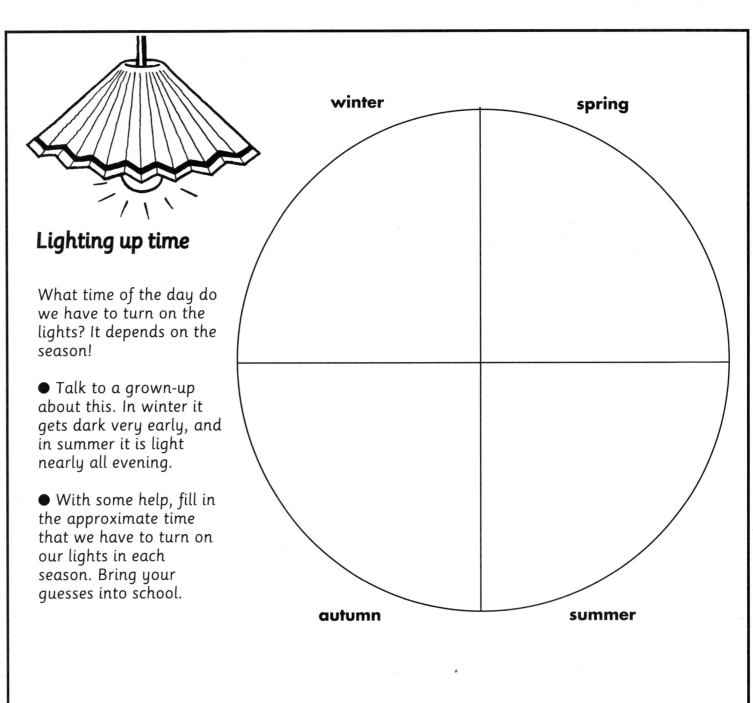

Lighting up time

What time of the day do we have to turn on the lights? It depends on the season!

● Talk to a grown-up about this. In winter it gets dark very early, and in summer it is light nearly all evening.

● With some help, fill in the approximate time that we have to turn on our lights in each season. Bring your guesses into school.

winter   spring

autumn   summer

How long did I take?

YOU WILL NEED: a clock or watch with a face, some Blu-Tack and a dice.

● You are going to find out how many minutes it takes to throw four 4s on a dice.

● Ask a grown-up to mark the clock with Blu-Tack on the place where the big hand is.

● Start throwing the dice. Throw it as fast as you can and as many times as you can. Count how many 4s you get. When you have got four 4s, stop throwing the dice.

● Ask the grown-up to mark the clock a second time with Blu-Tack.

● Together, study the clock and count how many minutes have passed. How far has the big hand moved? Write down the number of minutes and bring this into school.

Dear Parent or Carer

Talk about the fact that the big hand goes round the clock once an hour. How many minutes has it gone between the first and the second piece of Blu-Tack – it helps a lot if you can arrange things so that the first piece of Blu-Tack is on a number so that you are dealing with five-minute intervals.

_____and

child

_____

helper(s)

_____

did this activity together

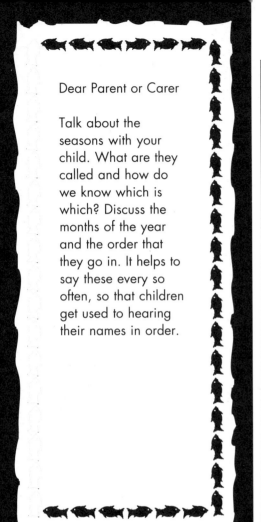

Dear Parent or Carer

Talk about the seasons with your child. What are they called and how do we know which is which? Discuss the months of the year and the order that they go in. It helps to say these every so often, so that children get used to hearing their names in order.

_____and

child

_____

helper(s)

_____

did this activity together

Seasonal sort-out

YOU WILL NEED: a set of cards, each one labelled with a month of the year. You can make these from the backs of old Christmas or birthday cards or cut up the back of an old cornflake packet.

● Turn the cards face down and put them in a pile.

● Take it in turns to take a card. Place it in the right space below, according to which season it is in. When all the cards are gone, count how many you have in each season.

spring

summer

autumn

winter

Day count!

- How many letters are there in each day of the week?

- Cut out the labels with the names of each day from the bottom of this page. Place them into sets according to the number of letters in each one. For example, Monday has 6 letters.

- Then put the labels in order – Sunday, Monday, and so on.

Sunday

Monday

Tuesday

Wednesday

Thursday

Friday

Saturday

Dear Parent or Carer

This activity is really to help children to think about the days of the week, and to learn how to spell them! Help them to write one or two of the days, but do not make them write them all. Write some for them. Talk about the order the labels should go in. Make larger labels and take the right one out each day and stick it on the wall.

_____and

child

_____

helper(s)

_____

did this activity together

_____and

child

_____

helper(s)

_____

did this activity together

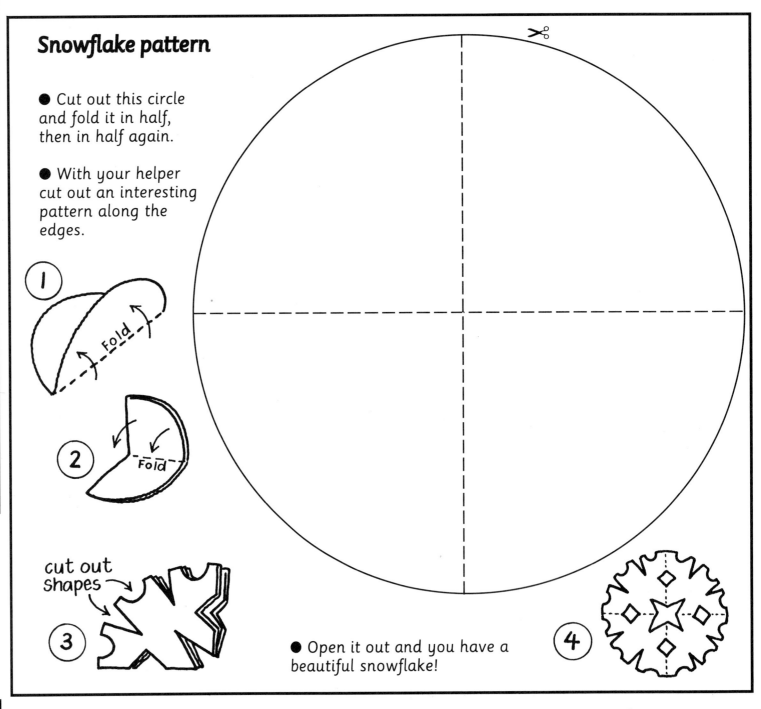

Snowflake pattern

● Cut out this circle
and fold it in half,
then in half again.

● With your helper
cut out an interesting
pattern along the
edges.

① Fold

② Fold

cut out
shapes

③

● Open it out and you have a
beautiful snowflake!

④

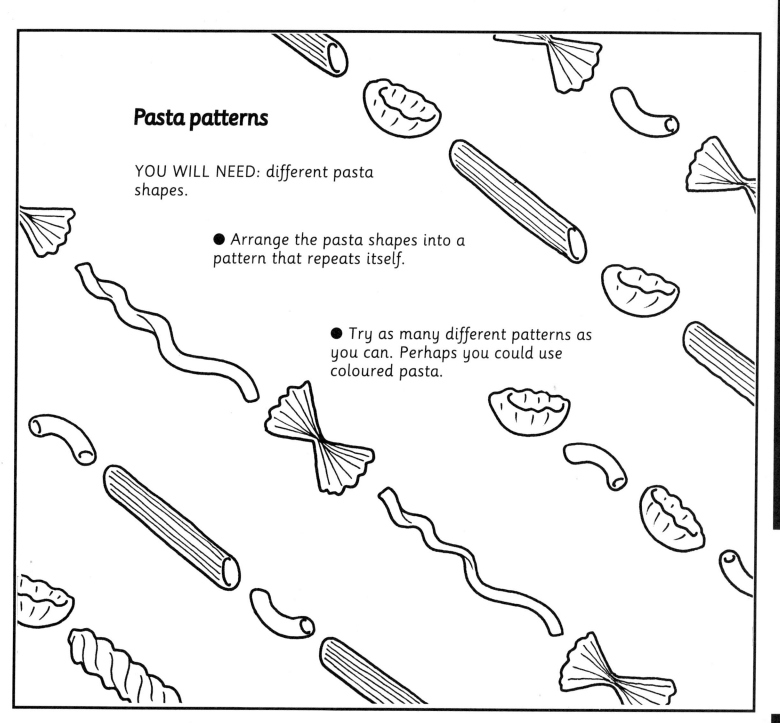

Pasta patterns

YOU WILL NEED: *different pasta shapes.*

● Arrange the pasta shapes into a pattern that repeats itself.

● Try as many different patterns as you can. Perhaps you could use coloured pasta.

Dear Parent or Carer

Please give your child time to experiment with different repeating patterns. They may like to thread the shapes to make a bracelet. Your child may prefer to use other objects to make a repeating pattern, for example conkers, bottle tops, leaves, LEGO and so on.

_____and

child

_____

helper(s)

_____

did this activity together

impact MATHS HOMEWORK

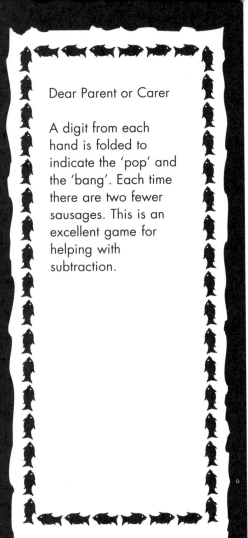

_____and

child

_____

helper(s)

_____

did this activity together

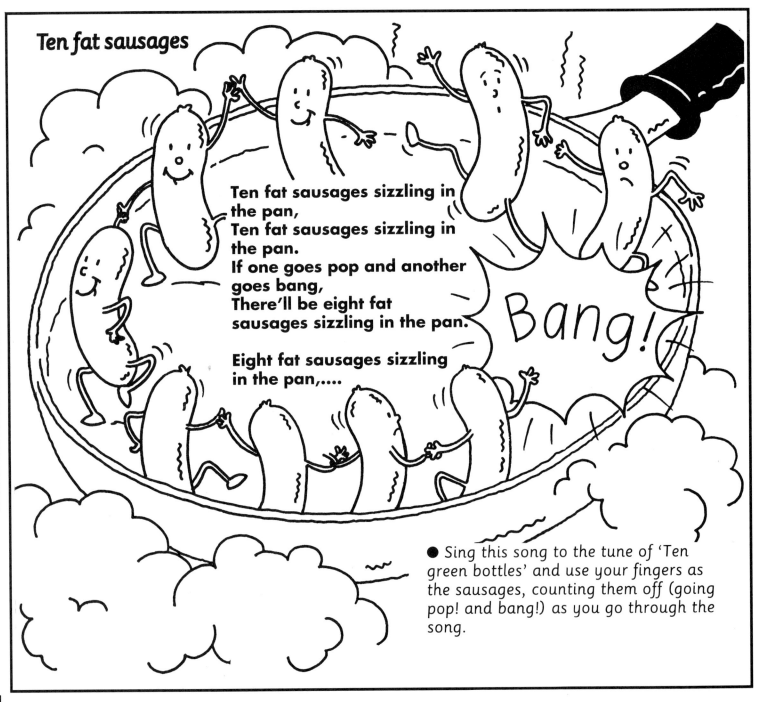

Ten fat sausages

**Ten fat sausages sizzling in the pan,
Ten fat sausages sizzling in the pan.
If one goes pop and another goes bang,
There'll be eight fat sausages sizzling in the pan.**

Eight fat sausages sizzling in the pan,....

Bang!

● Sing this song to the tune of 'Ten green bottles' and use your fingers as the sausages, counting them off (going pop! and bang!) as you go through the song.

Clapping names

● Clap these names below – one clap
for each part of the name.

Re   bec   ca

1   **2**   **3**   **claps**

Pe   ter

1   **2**   **claps**

Ben

1 clap

● How many claps does your name
have?

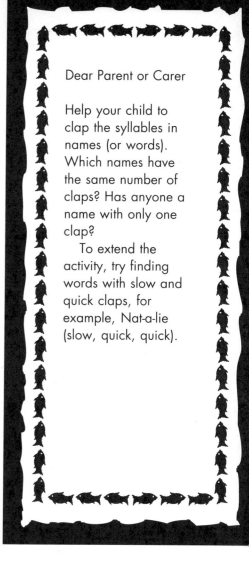

Dear Parent or Carer

Help your child to
clap the syllables in
names (or words).
Which names have
the same number of
claps? Has anyone a
name with only one
clap?

   To extend the
activity, try finding
words with slow and
quick claps, for
example, Nat-a-lie
(slow, quick, quick).

_____and

child

_____

helper(s)

_____

did this activity together

impact MATHS HOMEWORK

_____and

child

_____

helper(s)

_____

did this activity together

Design a patchwork quilt

● Cut out and arrange these shapes to fit together into a repeating pattern, like a patchwork quilt.

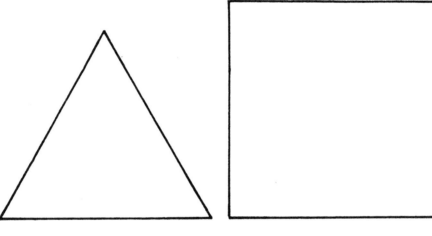
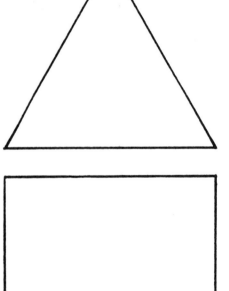
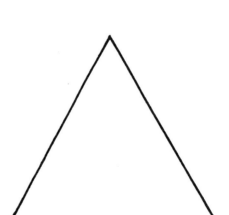
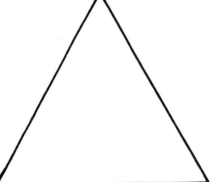

impact MATHS HOMEWORK

Sorting leaves

● With your helper, gather between five and ten leaves.

● Sort the leaves into these sets:

**Shiny leaves/Dull leaves
Rough leaves/Smooth leaves
Dark green/Light green
Jagged edges/Smooth edges,
and so on.**

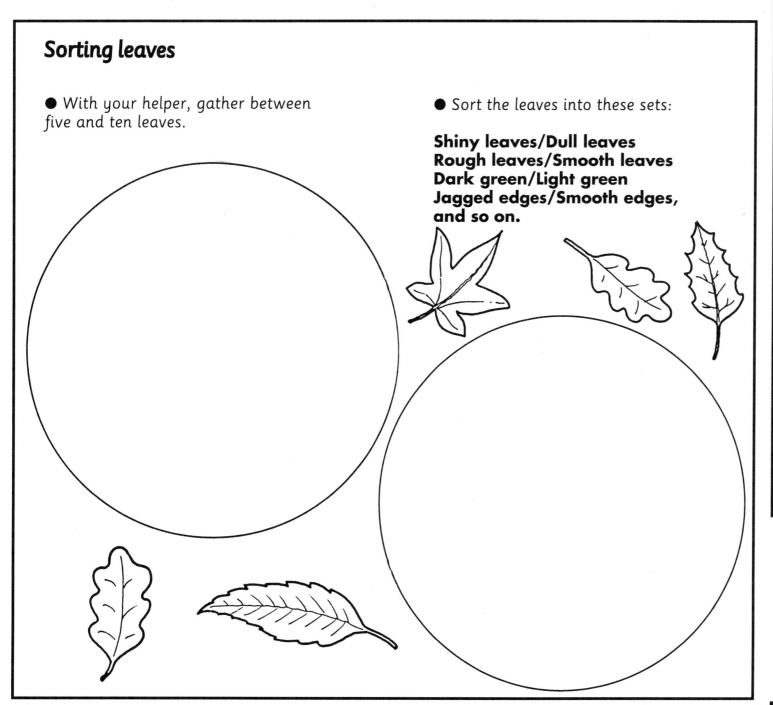

Dear Parent or Carer

There are many other categories, please help your child to be imaginative.

_____and

child

_____

helper(s)

_____

did this activity together

How many legs?

● Can you sort these pictures? Cut them out and stick them into two sets: 'four legs' and 'not four legs'? Ask someone to help you.

impact MATHS HOMEWORK

Play the money game

YOU WILL NEED: a purse of coins (about ten 2p and 1p coins) each, a counter each, a 10p coin to toss, a bank of coins and someone to play with.

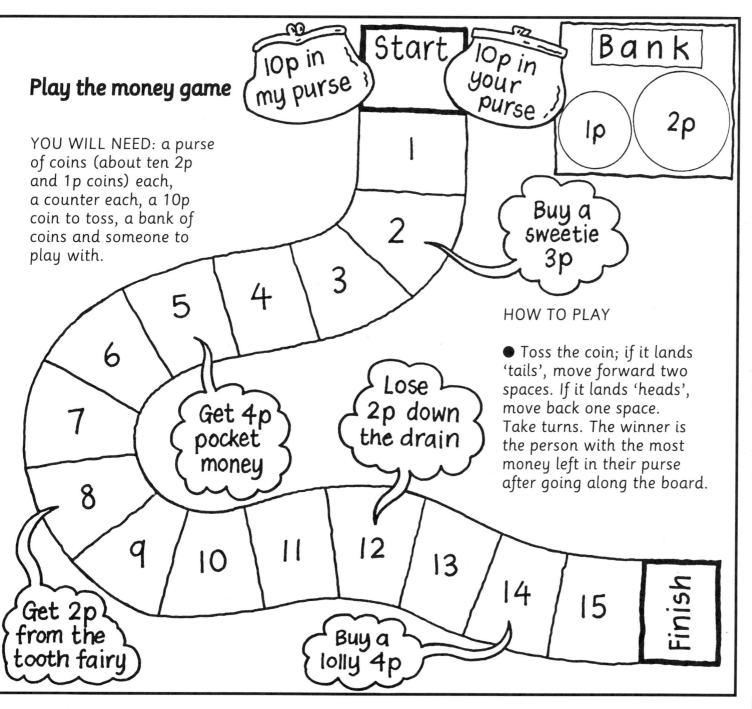

Start

10p in my purse

10p in your purse

Bank

1p   2p

1

2

Buy a sweetie 3p

3

4

5

6

7

8

Get 4p pocket money

Lose 2p down the drain

9

10

11

12

13

14

15

Finish

Get 2p from the tooth fairy

Buy a lolly 4p

HOW TO PLAY

● Toss the coin; if it lands 'tails', move forward two spaces. If it lands 'heads', move back one space. Take turns. The winner is the person with the most money left in their purse after going along the board.

_____and

child

_____

helper(s)

_____

did this activity together

_____and

child

_____

helper(s)

_____

did this activity together

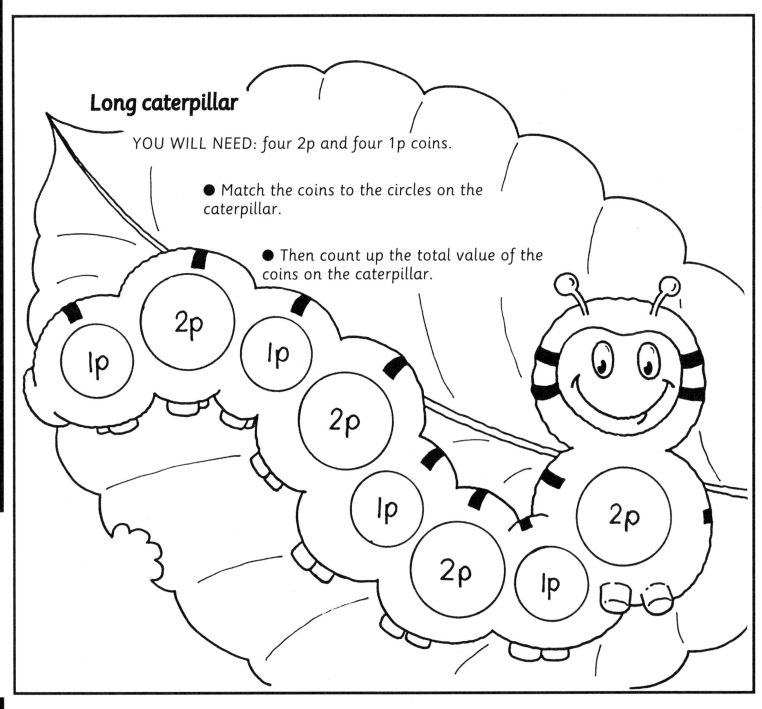

Long caterpillar

YOU WILL NEED: *four 2p and four 1p coins.*

● Match the coins to the circles on the caterpillar.

● Then count up the total value of the coins on the caterpillar.

impact MATHS HOMEWORK

Box shapes

● Find an interesting box and draw each side (face) on to a sheet of paper. Cut out the shapes and sort them into families.

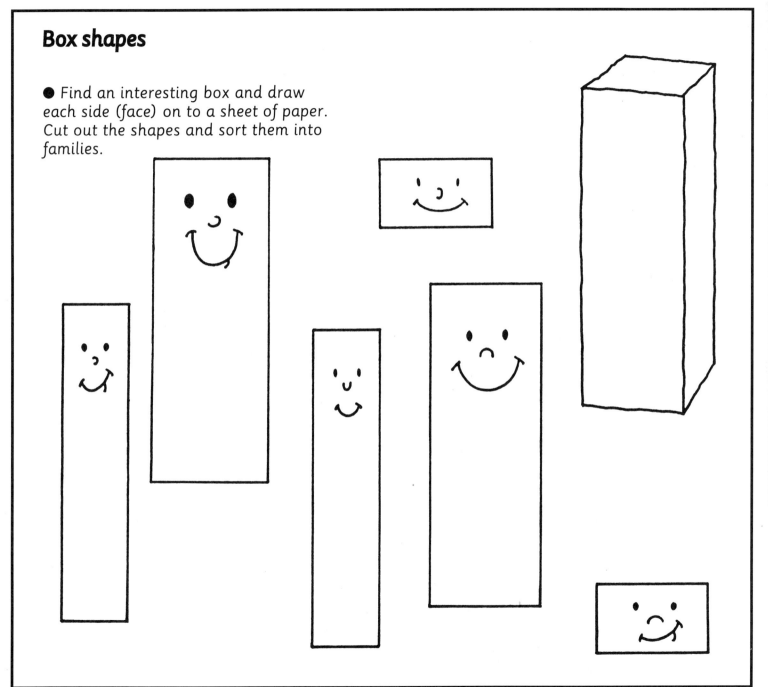

Dear Parent or Carer

Help your child to find a box with unusual sides (faces). When you have cut out each shape help your child to sort them in different ways, by size or shape.

_____and

child

_____

helper(s)

_____

did this activity together

Going shopping

● *Fill in these gaps:*

I saw a _____ at the shop.

I needed these coins to buy it:

I saw a _____ at the shop.

I needed these coins to buy it:

I saw a _____ at the shop.

I needed these coins to buy it:

I saw a _____ at the shop.

I needed these coins to buy it:

impact MATHS HOMEWORK

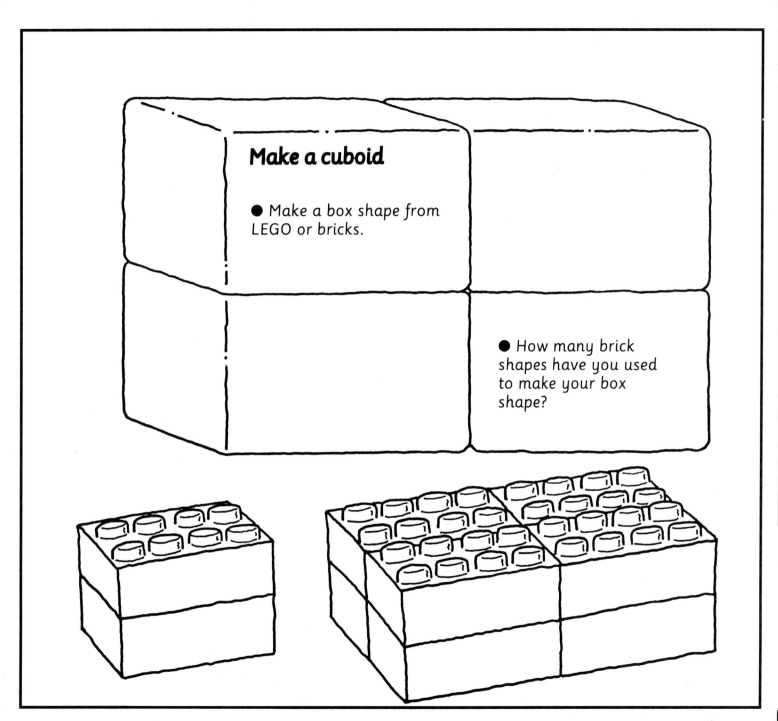

Make a cuboid

● Make a box shape from LEGO or bricks.

● How many brick shapes have you used to make your box shape?

Dear Parent or Carer

Encourage your child to look at the shape of boxes. Discuss the fact that each box has several faces, and talk about the shapes of the faces; are they square faces, or triangular faces or oblong faces? Help your child to arrange the bricks into a shape and count how many bricks have been used.

_____and

child

_____

helper(s)

_____

did this activity together

impact MATHS HOMEWORK

_____and

child

_____

helper(s)

_____

did this activity together

Beautiful butterfly

● Fold the paper along the dotted line,
then cut out the butterfly shape.

● Colour and cut out the small shapes
and stick them on to your butterfly in
such a way that both sides are exactly
the same.

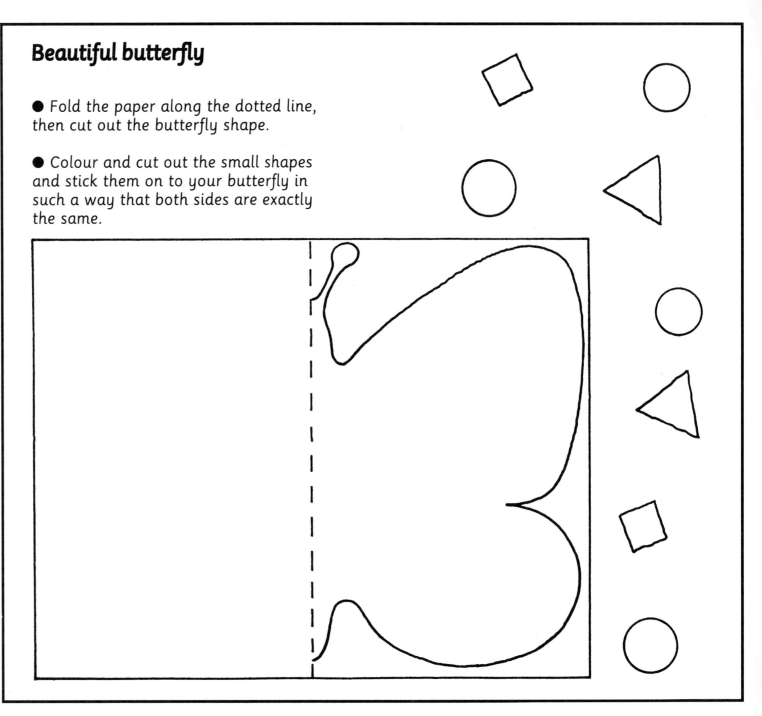

Cylinders

● Look at the cylinders below.

● Now design something that will move using cylinders.

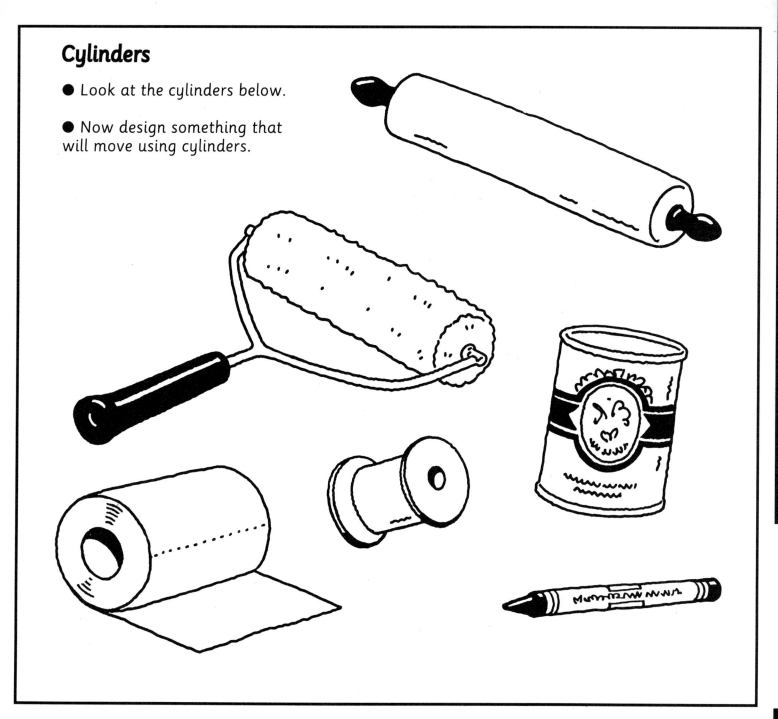

Dear Parent or Carer

Help your child to choose some cylinders (yoghurt pots, insides of toilet rolls, cotton reels and so on). Encourage them to roll the cylinders and make suggestions as to how they could be used to make simple models.

_____and

child

_____

helper(s)

_____

did this activity together

_____and

child

_____

helper(s)

_____

did this activity together

Favourite car colours

● Ask friends and family to help
you by each colouring in one of these
cars in their favourite colour.

● Sort the cars into sets according
to colour.

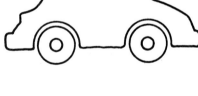

impact MATHS HOMEWORK